WALK SOFT IN THE FOLD

WALK SOFT IN THE FOLD

DAVID B. NIXON

Illustrated by Mary Williams

1977

CHATTO & WINDUS

LONDON

Published by
Chatto & Windus Ltd
40 William IV Street
London WC2N 4DF
*
Clarke, Irwin & Co. Ltd.
Toronto

British Library Cataloguing in Publication Data
Nixon, David, B
    Walk soft in the fold.
    ISBN 0-7011-2216-1
    1. Title
    636. '0092'4 SF375.5.G7
    Nixon, David B

Printed in Great Britain by
Redwood Burn Ltd
Trowbridge & London

Dedicated to the memory of
PIERS DAVID,
our mongol son who brought with him
Love, Light and Peace.
15th September, 1971 — 14th March, 1975

CONTENTS

OXFORDSHIRE

INTERLUDE

GALLOWAY DAYS

COTSWOLD SPUR

Acknowledgements

It gives me great joy to place on record my indebtedness to the late Roger Williams of Berkhamsted, who with great patience and kindness first taught me to see and appreciate the seasons' pageant of beauty in this green island.

And to thank his daughter, Anna, now my wife, for her sympathy, encouragement and long labours at the typewriter, without which this book would have remained unwritten.

PROLOGUE

Up in the sunlit fold a lamb was crying, and the fern at the woodside put out its crook to hold the Summer in. As I stood in the graveyard grass close-hemmed by stone, a ewe made answer, mouthing her cry from a throat made thick with love.

And the words on the little old headstone with a date below them were become as the nonsense talked by men who speak of life and death as beginning and ending. As the voice of Edgar spoke as one with the lamb and the answering ewe.

'Stop darting about loike one o' they blue-arsed flize and larn ter walk soft in the fold!'

So I'll try to say the unsayable, be an Aaron to Moses like, and paint you a portrait of the shepherd — Edgar Kirby.

THE CHILTERNS

1. *First Meeting*

I met him first on a February morning. It was just after seven, dark and thick with a swirling mist. My first day on the farm and my boots were big, new and very heavy. The foreman had seen me at my lodgings the previous night.

'I'm putting you with the sheep for the first few days. You'll be working with Edgar. He's rough-tongued, but a good man with the sheep. Get on with Edgar and you'll get on with anyone! Seven o'clock in Tunnel Field — be sharp!'

The grass was wet about my feet. Tunnel Field had no boundaries but walls of mist. Up ahead of me sheep were calling. I groped uncertainly towards the sound. A figure loomed out of the mist — Edgar! I suppose he did change his clothes sometimes, but this morning and all the fair mornings I remember him, he was dressed the same. Not a big man, but gnarled and chunky, like an old thorn — he grew out of the soil. Not an alien like myself, but as much part of the scene as the hurdles he stood beside, the prong he held in his root-brown hands, and the grey rain-misted sheep that milled about him.

A battered, bandless trilby, green with age was clamped over grizzled untidy hair, and a face wizened like an old apple, brown in the box. Sharp blue eyes regarded me in silent questioning. He was enveloped in a tattered raincoat fastened with a multitude of leather straps. Edgar's 'Zealand' coat and, as I was to learn through many seasons, his pride and joy. What I could see of his legs were bound in sacking strips tied with billy band, down to great steel-shod boots.

Edgar spoke, or rather rasped, 'Ye'll be ter new feller. Throw 'em' (he jerked his head towards the yelling sheep) 'fifty dacent mangels, then split 'em.'

He shoved the 'prong', with its two shining spears, into my uncertain hand. Over-eager I lunged into the heap of

17

mangolds in the pen, impaled two and made a vain attempt to fling them amongst the flock. The mangolds remained transfixed and I nearly tore my insides out.

'Wert!' growled Edgar. 'Give us 'ere.'

He took the prong and with a deft movement of his foot, held the mangolds down and removed the prong.

'Now watch and larn,' said the old man.

With a movement so easy, that the long-handled fork seemed but an extension of himself, he slid the prongs upturned into the heap of roots, without pausing, his arm described an arc and two orange mangolds sped into the misty field. Again and again the fork flashed and soon mangolds were scattered everywhere.

'Roight,' he said, sticking the fork into a bale of hay, 'now ye can split 'em.'

Edgar took a weird looking instrument, two half moons of iron dovetailed together, their edges forming a cross blade of metal and mounted on a thick shaft. He brought it down with a crack on the nearest mangold, scattering the sheep already trying to bite it, and four quarters fell, white flowers on the grey grass; then turning, he thrust it into my eager hands.

'I'll be up at lambin' yard, close by Holly Bush. Be sharp as ye can.'

He strode away into the skirts of mist and was lost to sight.

I set to work with a will, until a bed of flowers lay upon the grass — cold white in the growing light of morning — whilst the sheep followed me around, running greedily from morsel to fresh morsel.

I placed the 'splitter' back in the pen and walked towards the lambing yard, already I could see the dark bulk of Holly Bush against the paling sky across the field.

Tunnel Field was immense and sloped from North to South. Along the Northern boundary ran an avenue of giant beech trees — 'grey goddesses' — as I was to come to call and love them. A tangled 'bullfinch' of a hedge ran down the eastern edge of Holly Bush, where the lambing yard had been built, snug in the southernmost corner.

As I walked I noticed that the field had been drilled,

also from North to South, in patterns of alternating rows of roots and a tall, green, leafy crop. Then I came to a wire fence supported by stakes. I climbed over, the ground was slippery and the strong scent of sheep hit my nostrils. I found myself stumbling over rows of white chewed stalks that protruded from the earth like jagged dirty teeth.

Further up the field I could see a row of brown hurdles, built of wicker-like material, resembling thick basket-work; these stretched across to another wire fence. This I swarmed over and found myself close to a brown weather-beaten caravan. From under the wheels a collie rose up and yikkered at me, rolling amber eyes and baring white fangs. I veered hastily away and saw Edgar standing by the straw bales which formed the wall of the lambing yard.

'Us'll gie the ewes theer bait afore brakefust. Iver put kettle on. Cum along with we.'

He stomped off towards the brown hurdles, stopping beside two great tin bins. Flinging back the lid of one he took out a bag and swung it over his shoulder.

'Go turn they trows over,' he barked, pointing to two lines of upturned troughs over the wire fence.

I straddled the wire.

'Na! Na!' he cried. 'Allus unloose the top wire from the stake, then ye doant stretch it.'

I did as I was bidden and hurried over to the troughs, eager to show my worth. By the time I had finished, the ewes were skittering round Edgar. He reached the first trough and dropping the bag to the ground untwisted the neck, then he swung the bag under his arm and using the wide neck as a funnel began scattering the corn and nuts along the row.

As he did so he yelled, 'Fetch I the other bag from the bin, lad.'

Away I darted and in no time was standing by the second line.

'Righto doant stand gawpin', teem it in.'

I copied Edgar's movements and did just that, practically the whole bag shot uncontrolled into the first trough as the ewes jostled round me.

'Praper cack-handed aint ye,' growled the old man.

19

'Never mind ye'll larn.'

And 'larn' I did over the next weeks, until I could swing the bag of corn under my arm and by subtle adjustment of the neck of the bag, tightening it or letting it go slack, I learnt how to control the flow of corn. I also learnt very quickly the trick of putting a mere shatter of corn into the first trough, leaving the ewes to mill around it whilst I filled the other trough unhindered by a scrum of ewes.

Whilst the ewes fed, Edgar moved through a gap in the hurdles and up through the muddy fold to another line of hurdles quite different from the brown wicker ones behind. They looked like gates and Edgar bent forward a stake and released a loop of thick twine from the top of a hurdle, then swung the hurdle open, moving across the gap he had made, he pulled the stake up and swung back a second hurdle.

'Roight,' he grunted, 'they'll soon find their new grub. We'll go and get owern.'

As we walked down the fold the ewes were already streaming away from the trough.

'Why do you use different kinds of hurdles?' I asked the old man.

He stopped and pointed to the hurdles we had just opened.

'Those be gate 'urdles. Easy to lug about and nice ter pitch but they don't keep the wind back.'

He nodded towards the brown wicker-like hurdles I had noticed earlier.

'They be basket 'urdles, 'eavy an' the devil ter snag yer jacket on, but masterful fer givin' lambs a bit er burrer. They coom wi' we from 'ampshire. 'Nuff talkin', we're behind time a'ready. Go an' turn they trows ower again. Then away fer brakefust.'

When I reached the caravan Edgar had already poured out two mugs of steaming brown tea. I sat on the top step and he passed me an opened tin of condensed milk and grunted ' 'elp yoursen.' He sat on a low box with a sacking cushion; bread and cheese clutched in one claw of a hand and a knife in the other, expertly flicking bread and cheese into his mouth, now and again sending a chunk flying towards the collie, which lay at the foot of the steps.

I took off my gloves, they were new and I was very proud of them, particularly the yellow leather facings. A wind had got up, rolling the mist back, but it was cold and raw. I blew on my fingers before opening my pack of sandwiches.

The old man's voice broke in on my thoughts.

'What do ye want they var?' He was looking scornfully at my gloves, now lying on the step.

'Tis up ter you I s'pose but tis not the way ter git yer 'ands 'ard or keep 'em warm fer that matter.'

I quickly changed the subject. 'Do you turn the troughs over every day — even when it's dry?'

Edgar smiled, obviously pleased at my interest. 'If yer leave 'em up, then sheep paddle the muck into 'em, 'specially when lambs are about, little tackers play in 'em. Then agin wet trows git sour and spoil the grub.'

We both fell to eating and drinking the sweet strong tea. From the canal in the valley a barge put-putted through the mist, which still clung, a grey winding wreath upon the water.

2. *Lambing Yard*

We swilled the mugs in a bucket of rain water and made ready to leave the shelter of the shepherd's hut.

'Reckon we'll take a turn round the pens afore goin' up ter the fold,' said Edgar as he fastened the top half of the van door.

Entrance into the lambing yard was by way of two straw thatched gate hurdles. About thirty ewes were scattered around the centre yard, some of them pulling at wooden racks of hay, others clearing up pieces of mangold. A line of hurdles hung with canvas separated this main yard from a large pen under the dutch barn, which was still stacked with hay at one end. Some twenty ewes ran in this pen with their lambs. Round the open yard on three sides a row of pens had been built of hurdles. A roof of thatched hurdles, protected them from the weather. They looked very snug, with the wall of straw bales behind them.

A ewe and her lamb (or lambs) occupied most of these nursery pens. Edgar was speaking and I pricked up my ears.

'The ewes in the yard 'ere are yet to lamb down. Under the barn we turn ewes with lambs that are sucking well. 'Elps 'em ter get their legs afore we put them out into the fold. These 'ere,' Edgar pointed to the pens, 'are the latest lambs.' He shook his head impatiently, 'Nar we must get on.'

I walked round the line of pens with him. At each one he bent over lifting out a wooden box and placing it upside down upon the roof. One ewe had hardly touched her corn, the old man climbed into the pen and felt the ewe's ears. I looked inquiringly at him.

'Ears are stone cold,' he said. 'Nip ower ter the 'edge and fetch an 'andful of ivy. That'll tempt 'er.'

By the time I returned he was well round the line of pens. I dropped the ivy into the ewe and went over to him.

'Coom in ter pen lad,' he said. 'Look at her bag — see how swelled the teat is. Lamb'll never suck that.' He began to strip the milk from the teat. 'Ketch the lamb and let's try un now.'

I held the lamb and struggled to point it to the teat. Each time I let go the lamb staggered off to the wrong end.

'Try ter hold its mouth open,' said Edgar. I did so and he sent a jet of milk down its throat. The lamb coughed and spluttered. At the next try the lamb took the teat into its mouth, sucking vigorously. In its eagerness to feed it lost the teat again but having once tasted the warm sweet milk, the lamb found it almost immediately.

'Little ole tacker'll be all right now,' said the old man, grinning delightedly. 'Just see they've all got clean water, lad, then we'll get inter the field.'

He glanced round the ewes in the yard. 'Nothing hurtin' 'ere. There's a bucket by the water barrel.'

3. *Setting the Fold*

The ewes were busily feeding in the kale and turnips. 'They're not very keen on the turnips,' I remarked.

'Oh they'll come to 'em presently,' said Edgar. 'But they'm that fond of a bit of fresh grass — an' those turnips be swedes!'

Suddenly I saw a group of lambs running about in the kale outside the fold. 'Some have got out Edgar,' I cried excitedly.

'They be a'right. I've got a lamb 'urdle set in that forrard row of gate 'urdles for lambs ter run through to get a pickin of the best grub.' He pointed out what looked at first sight like a garden gate, the bottom half consisting of widely placed slats — big enough for a lamb, but too narrow for the ewes, carrying as they did a heavy fleece.

'Dash it,' exclaimed Edgar. 'I've bin an' fergot the bar. 'Tis by that hut. Go an' fetch un lad. Reckon yer legs be younger than mine.'

I hurried away, not liking to show my ignorance of what a 'bar' was and hoping against hope that the missing object would be so obvious by the hut that my choice would at least be limited.

No such luck, the hut seemed to have gathered about it all manner of weird tools and implements. Some lying underneath, others propped against the wall. 'Two tine' forks I recognised. 'Five tine' dung forks, 'splitters' which I had met before. A peculiar hoe, with two flat tines or blades, looking like an angry bird with beak agape. A long-handled hammer which had two heads, each deeply cupped. . . . .

'What be at lad?' Edgar's voice had an edge of impatience. 'Yer be lookin' at the dern thing.'

I looked desperately, in front of me, close by the caravan wheel, I saw a brown iron pole about four feet long, driven into the ground. Its top was flattened and polished silver with long use. This must be a 'bar'. I tried to lift it on to my shoulder, but the 'bar' scarcely moved. It took a big heave and a hefty swing to get it on to my shoulder and by the time I reached Edgar I was glad to put it down.

It was then that I noticed the sharp point that 'klunked' into the ground, a point that ran back to a thick spear of metal, and then to the rounded shaft.

'Roight,' said Edgar. 'Take the bagging hook.' He handed me a small sickle. 'Cut a lane 'bout a yard wide, from this stake to that 'urdle that joins the two nets over there. Mind yer throw the roots and the kale downhill so that the ewes'll eat 'em in the next fold.'

I set to work. It was fairly easy to keep straight, because Edgar had set out the gate hurdles to be pitched in clumps of three between the two nets which ran up the field. Each clump of hurdles was propped by a stake, two other stakes lying against them.

The lane cleared I walked back to the shepherd, already moving across the fold with his line of hurdles.

'Good lad,' he said. 'Watch me and pass the 'urdles as I need 'em, one stake to each.'

As I watched, he moved the last hurdle he had set to one side, then with the 'bar' he made a hole for the toe, then swung the hurdle back and dropped it neatly into position, giving the end the lightest tap. He turned to me as he did this: 'Never bang 'urdles in, allus make a toe 'ole. Ye can tap ter settle it like, but banging splits the heads.

Then the old man, talking as he worked, continued my first lesson in hurdle pitching. 'First make a toe 'ole 'bout three inches in, topside the 'urdle. Now a stake.' He made a mark with the point of the stake about three inches away from the toe of the last hurdle, moved the stake and plunged the bar one-handed straight on to the mark. Again and again he shot the bar into the hole, working it this way and that until big enough to take the stake. 'Allus try ter slant yer stake 'ole a little toward yersel. Never toward yer 'urdle.' In plumped the stake. Deftly he slipped the next gate hurdle between stake and the head of the last, neatly dropping its far toe into the hole prepared, then sticking the bar in the ground he bent the stake with his body weight towards the head of the first hurdle, thus trapping the last addition to his wall between them. So quickly did he move that I did not see him put a loop of tarred twine over the stake but there it was, as if by magic, stretching from stake to the head of the first hurdle. As he released the stake, the loop took the strain and in tightening bound hurdle to hurdle.

Edgar moved back and made ready to repeat the process. 'The loops, Edgar?' He looked at me in puzzlement. 'Loops?' he questioned.

'These,' I said, touching the bundle of twine loops I now saw hanging from his belt.

'Shackles ye mean!' laughed Edgar. 'Ye'll usually see 'em 'anging on the 'urdles afore I pitches 'em. These (he touched the shackles at his waist) be new uns. Made of tarred twine they be. Rain rots 'em after a whiles, so I'm putting a new lot out for this row.'

'Na then.' He squinted along the row of hurdles so far pitched. 'Ye can 'ave a go now. Try ter keep yer line straight. A bowed fence is a weak fence and willna hold a press of sheep.' Edgar handed me the bar. 'One more thing afore I takes a look at they ewes in the yard; when yer pitchin' yer 'ole, stand wi yer feet well apart. Yon bar ud go straight through yer boot. An' use two 'ands with it, yer wrists be none too strong yet, I'm thinkin'.'

He moved away, whistling tunelessly, then turned and shouted over his shoulder. 'There'll be a cup o' tea, when ye've fettled yon lot.'

Painstakingly I copied the old man's method. The worst job was getting the bar to hit the same hole twice! Slowly I began to master it and became wholly absorbed in the rhythm of the work. Sometimes I found that I had pitched the hole too far out, so that the stake did not hug the hurdle the whole of its length. Now and again I pitched the hole at too sharp an angle and found that the shackle just would not reach. I soon began to realise that each stake had a character of its own. Some like the smooth grey sycamore had no 'give' in them; others (hazel) were much springier. Over the months that followed I came to recognize each set of stakes, and to see that the individual hurdles, often warped by rain, wind and sun, had definite minds of their own. As I mastered the 'technicalities' of pitching, I began to enjoy not only the job in hand but was able to look around and study the room in which I worked.

To mark the patterned clouds moving across the roof of the valley, the madcap capers of rooks pitchpoling over the fields, like scraps of torn black paper, and the starling swarms, wheeling with uncanny precision as they were disturbed in their foraging about the 'troughs', and always the beeches, singing the wind's song as they crowned Tunnel Field.

4. *Battle of the Nets*

Dinnertime came and went. Edgar surveyed my handiwork with the hurdles with a kindly but critical eye. 'Bit of a bend in it Davey. Try to keep 'em straight — nothing looks better in the fold, but it's fairish.'

This was high praise indeed as I was soon to learn.

'I'm going up ter the Sheephouse this arternoon,' said Edgar. 'Gotta see Harry 'bout some tackle for the ewes. Ye can roll up some o' they nets down the field. No need ter carry 'em all up 'ere; we'll 'ave the cart tomorrer. Jest roll 'em up an' mind yer leave the stakes tidy by each net, dunna mix 'em up.'

He loosed the collie from under the caravan. 'Heel Bob,' he yelled as the collie bounded towards me. The dog obeyed and the two made their way up the track and were soon lost to sight in the beech avenue.

I started work on the first net, which stretched for fifty yards downhill. I began at the bottom, which seemed logical enough, unthreaded each stake, letting the net drop to the ground away from me, then placed each stake back in its hole. So far so good; now to roll it up. Well, I had no need to carry them and it seemed pointless to walk back down, doing nothing. I began rolling the net downhill. I shall never forget it. The wire net seemed alive. In no time it was chest high and bouncing all over the place. If it hadn't been for the stumps of kale, catching in the net, it would have run away altogether. I finished up with fifty yards of wire netting, almost as high as myself, looking something like a gigantic telescope.

Ah well, that's one done I thought, glad to turn my

attention to the stakes, my hands cold because the gloves were sodden wet. Edgar wanted each set of stakes by their own net, so be it. I walked up the field 'doing nothing' turned and began to pick up the stakes. I found that I couldn't carry more than six or seven at a time and even then they slipped all over the place. I tried leaning them against the folded net, but it was too big. I gave up and let them lie on the ground beside it. I tackled three more nets. A twenty-five yarder ran along the bottom of the old fold; this was more like it and I felt that I had made a better job of rolling it. The other two were brutes — 'fifty yarders' — again running up the hill. These were taller nets. The stakes were not threaded through the wire but stood outside it and the wire was hung on two hooks, top and bottom of each stake.

They were much easier to drop and this time I decided to roll them uphill. The wire kept tighter but time and again it got caught upon the old chewed kale stalks. Each time I lifted the roll to release it, the wire sprang round like a clock spring suddenly released, often trapping my fingers. I had long since discarded my gloves, and my hands were whipped red by the wind and bleeding from the snagging wire. I loathed the job and was so relieved to start collecting the stakes, that I thoroughly mixed the two sets up and threw them into one heap. My last bright idea was to roll the top hook net, down to the first so that they could be picked up more easily by the cart in the morning; then with a sigh of relief I walked back to the hut, thinking to have a cup of tea in peace. After all, I'd done what Edgar had asked me.

'Hey!' A voice checked my feet. 'Where be going?' It was Edgar. He was moving faster than I would have thought possible and heading my way. I sensed trouble.

'What do ye call that?' He pointed with withering scorn to my first effort.

'A net,' I said helpfully.

Edgar's face was a picture, talk about an angry sunset! 'A net is it — ye means wuz afore ye got ye fancy 'ands on it.'

'An' they?' he wagged his head towards the other

27

monsters, his trilby nearly parting company with his grey thatch. 'An' I s'pose I told ye ter lay the stakes in the mud!' he added for good measure as he spotted them. 'Tea wor it ye were thinkin' of? Time enuff for that when ye've larnt ter do a job proper. Coom 'we!'

Shamefaced I joined him by the nets. Edgar lifted one of the hook nets clear of the stakes about it. He untwisted the wires which I had so painstakingly twisted up to fasten it down, and with a flick sent the net spinning and unrolling down the hill. 'Na,' he said, 'get ter the bottom end an' pull it out straight.' I did so in silence. When I looked up Edgar had fastened the top end by replacing the end stake and was striding downhill towards me.

'Roight. Now watch me.' He bent down and picked up the net. 'First, pull ter net tight.' As he spoke, he heaved at the fifty yards of net. 'Now bend yer end in tight ter make a core like and twist the inside wire ter hold it. Now roll.' He began rolling the wire up the hill. 'Watch how I keeps it straight by moving me 'ands first to the left, if she's pulling right, or right if she's pulling left.' He stopped and holding the roll tightly, lifted it clear of the ground and heaved at it again. 'Keep pulling it tight.' As I watched I could see the roll tighten round the core. 'Then on agin.' Edgar finished the net. It was tight and neat, about 2 ft. or a little more in diameter. He finished off by twisting the end wire in, top, bottom and middle. To prove his point he lifted it high in the air and bounced it down; the net didn't move or lose its tightness. 'Na,' he said, 'fifty stakes to lean agin it.' I hastened to help him. Then he turned to me. 'See they others? Roll 'em out and roll 'em up agin and then we'll see about tea.' No more was said. Edgar walked off grinning and I fell to. Even today, years later, his voice still booms in my ears. 'Roll 'em out and roll 'em up agin' and he was right.

5. *Racking Up*

By the time I had finished the nets, the light was going. No sunset sky but grey mist creeping up from the canal as if to choke the day. I could hear a barge thumping resonantly in the lock, the voices of bargees, a lock key ringing upon the stone coping and the rattle of the ratchet running. I was wet, muddy, tired and yet contented as I turned wearily towards the caravan.

'Cup o' tea Davey,' called Edgar. I climbed the steps and took the mug of sweet scalding tea into my hands. The old man looked at them and grunted 'Ah see ye got rid o' they gloves. Yer hands'll soon harden. Here!' He reached down a tin from the shelf. 'Rub some of this salve into the cuts — don't wanna git the frost into 'em.' The tin was marked 'Udder Ointment' but I took it without comment.

'Now drink yer tea an' git warm by the stove. I'll go an' rack up the ewes in the yard. Iver done the pens. Coom an' see me when yer ready an' I'll show ye how ter fill a rack. Then ye can hay the tegs on yer way home.'

I hadn't a clue what tegs were but I nodded over my tea, nearly spilling it, and he was away down the steps.

As soon as I had finished my tea I joined Edgar in the lambing yard. 'Fetch I another truss of hay,' he called. 'No, not from the barn, that's baled hay. Under the sheet near the gate.'

I had started towards the barn but at his instruction turned back to the gate. The trusses were neat and easy to handle, about fifty-six pounds, perhaps less. I carried one over and dropped it near the upturned racks. The two strings were tied with a neat slip knot. I untied them and, doubling the strings, stuck them in my belt.

'Ye're larnin',' grinned Edgar approvingly. 'Never leave binder twine lying about the yard or the fold, it's death ter lambs.'

The hay racks were like long rib cages, hazel I would guess, each rib end slotted into a flat base which, upended as they were, looked like long narrow rectangles. A strut across the middle gave stability and this was reinforced by a long slat which ran along the curved ridge and kept the ribs equidistant like the breast bone.

With a 'two tine' fork Edgar began whisking the hay into the rack, each slide of hay folded naturally into place until the rack was full, then reaching out the fork he turned the rack-over and turned to fill the next.

The moment will always stay with me, for I had never realised until then how hay keeps the Summer in. Here on a late Winter afternoon with black ash branches scratching the roof of the barn, with mud in the fold and ice in the wind's breath, came a gust of Summer.

'Better be off now, time's goin' on! Give tegs a bale of hay. I was fergetting they've gart two iron racks. Just slide the roof back and fill 'em. Mind yer shake the hay out and see both are full.'

'Why do you call them 'tegs' Edgar?'

'Tegs?' He looked puzzled. 'Oh! that be what I der call last year's lambs. Be off now. See you in t'marning'. Mind yer give 'em fifty mangels as ye coom through.'

My first day was almost over. I was very tired but very happy as I left the tegs milling round the hay racks. I was no longer on the wrong side of the hedge — I belonged.

6. *Feeling my Feet*

The days and weeks that followed were full and hard. I had long ceased to notice the nagging weight of my boots, they fitted my feet and felt at home. Gum boots which had rubbed the backs of my legs raw were part of me. The yellow gloves had been chewed up long ago by Bob, who was quick to find them under the caravan where I had thrown them, sodden and useless. My hands were calloused with pitching hurdles, as I looked at them reflectively, I remembered the interest Edgar had shown in them. It happened one morning while we were having a mug of tea and a smoke. 'Ye wanna look arter yer 'ands, Davey. If yer gonna be a sheepman them small 'ands like yourn'll be a real blessing.' Talk had turned to other things with the arrival of Harry, the Head Shepherd, and I hadn't got round to asking what he had meant.

Edgar talked to me far more now, always about sheep and sheepman, but for days he would be wrapped up in a world of his own. 'Ise jest thinkin'' he would say if I tried to draw him out and if I unwisely persisted he'd snap 'Jawin' gits yer nowheres Davey, let's be gettin' on.'

The bailiff's few days with the sheep had become an indefinite time. One Friday evening as I collected my pay the bailiff said 'Edgar wants ter keep you with him and that's rare praise from that old cuss. How do you feel?'

'Oh yes,' I said. 'It's grand with the sheep.'

'That's settled then,' he said. 'You'll not find a better man to learn under.'

I got the handle 'the shepherd boy' and I was proud of it.

7. Harrowing

Spring came to the Chiltern Hills and I was sent to help Mr. Finch with the horses. The Winter corn had to be harrowed, to break up the Winter crust; later on I had to go over the same corn with the ring-roll to firm the young plants down. It was a job that I grew to love and, of course, for a green youngster the job was ideal. I had plenty of room to manoeuvre in a twenty or twelve acre field. At any rate that is what I thought. Mr. Finch set me to work, showing me how to hold the reigns. 'Don't ee worry if yer miss a bit,' he grinned. 'There's nothin' spoiling. Take three, may be four, turns round the headland, then start goin' up an' down. Let Dolly,' he motioned to the old Shire mare, 'take 'er time. Them new fangled tractors goes too fast, silly fast I calls it. Give yer harrows time to do the work.' He turned to leave me. 'I'll see yer back at the stable. Loose out about half three and bring the harrows back on the cart.' I was impatient to get started and Mr. Finch saw it in my restive attitude. 'Yer like a young colt. Reckon ye'll be tame time night comes.'

He was gone and I was off. I soon saw the sense in leaving a wide headland, in my inexperience I would often go too near the hedge and have insufficient room to turn round. The three harrows took a surprising wide sweep and quite a few times I gave a frantic 'Whoah' and had to pull the harrows back to squeeze round by the hedge. At dinnertime I gave Dolly her nosebag and sat under the hedge. I had bread and cheese, a large onion, and a large bottle of cold tea, sweet but without milk.

The field I was harrowing was called Spinney Field, after the deep spinney in one corner, from which the great grey trunks of the beech trees soared. Already the clawlike buds were breaking and many of the lower branches were spread with light green trays of leaf.

I was soon on my way again. Walking about a mile to the acre, I was bent upon finishing the field of sixteen acres before 'half three'. I did this and looked with contentment at the alternating bands of light and dark green corn. Light where the corn was going away, dark as it bent towards me.

With some difficulty I put the pad and britching harness on to Dolly and got her into the shafts of the cart. I fastened the tugs, the short chains for drawing or pulling to the shafts, and lifted the harrows and whipple-tree onto the cart, then we were away back to the farm. I felt full of confidence and entered the farmyard gate with a flourish and a loud bang! Sick with apprehension I saw the gatepost crack. Bill, the carpenter, emerged from his workshop with a grin. 'Don't fret young un. There's allus a first time for everythin'. P'rhaps they'll listen now. Only a fool sets gate-posts in concrete. No "give" yer see.'

Chastened, I loosed Dolly out of the cart and turned her into the stable.

I'd never watched Spring come before. Each day brought new beauty. In the evenings I'd walk up to the Hollow and listen enraptured to four nightingales singing not a mile from the village. They sang from the moonlit thorns, pink and white with blossom, and over and above them came the constant drone of night bombers. Wave after wave of Lancasters and Liberators going out to spill death and probably meet death over the Continent. Often in the early morning we would watch many limping back low over the hills, dragging themselves home.

8. *Milking*

I learnt to milk. Landgirls were helping us. My first morning in the cowshed was memorable. I took up the three-legged stool allotted to me and, resplendent in white smock, walked down behind the cows. Edna, a bright-faced girl, called 'Here, David.' I bent down, she was busy milking and milk was thrumming into the frothy pail. She kissed me on the cheek. I felt myself go scarlet and started back. She laughed and sent a jet of milk straight into my face. 'Milker's baptism,' she laughed.

Joe, the herdsman, set me to milk Buttercup, a quiet Shorthorn with great liquid brown eyes. Joe put her dairy-cake in the trough and showed me how to wash and dry her udder; then he took an aluminium cup with a black bakelite top. He took a squirt from each teat, each time letting the milk run across the bakelite into the cup. 'If you see any crumbs of milk, or clots, let me know,' he said. 'Now sit against her. Keep close — the closer you are the less she can kick you. Not that she will, she's as good as gold.'

I groped for the teats, one, two, three, I searched desperately for the fourth teat. Perhaps this cow was different? From the man milking beyond me came a great guffaw. 'Can't ye find 'em all, David?' and Fred released the fourth teat he'd been holding.

At first I pulled in vain. Joe watched me then said quietly, 'You're not bell ringing you know. Learn to squeeze the fingers in turn from the top — one, two, three, four — and be firm, don't tickle her, girls are ticklish customers!"

I was thankful when the milking ended. I had milked two cows and my wrists ached like bad toothache.

Two weeks later I was milking happily, in addition to which I could take aim and hit the target, usually one of the farm cats, with the same accuracy. When the herdsman wasn't looking, of course. The target would lick itself clean with great relish and come back for more.

Pride comes before a fall. Mine was both violent and precipitous. I was milking to Buttercup's complete satisfaction and mine. A fly settled on her flank, I gazed at it absentmindedly and did the obvious — I swatted it. Buttercup did likewise. In a flash of stars, the shooting variety, and a crash of metal, I lay in the dung channel, soaked in muck and milk, gazing apprehensively at Buttercup's rear end. She turned her head, chewing complacently, and surveyed me, coughed, but not politely, and added a very cowlike insult to injury.

9. *Long Piccott*

One evening in late Spring, Mr. Faulkner came down to the cottage in which I lodged. 'I'd like you to go with Edgar tomorrow. He's folding in Long Piccott, so don't bother to come up for milking, go straight to him first thing. The field lies just by the canal. It's almost on your doorstep.'

My face must have shown my delight.

Faulkner smiled, 'As a matter of fact, the old man asked for you and that's a rare compliment.'

We got the folds pitched forward and were a couple of days ahead. Edgar was delighted, the lambs were going ahead on the rape and turnips and cleaning up well. It wasn't until the second week that I realised that we were not alone in the field. Long Piccott lies between the canal and the little River Bulborne and to the South the river made a wide meander, leaving a sizeable pocket of land. This was fenced off and as we drew level with the sheep I could see several wire-netting pens and hen houses.

One day I was pitching a net right along the boundary of the smallholding. At least I was trying to pitch the holes for the net. It was like making holes six inches deep in a metal roadway. The metal bar bounced and jarred my arms. Normally I could hold the stake in one hand and drive the stake hole with the pointed bar. Now I was driven to using both hands. 'Get in,' I breathed, sweat trickling into my eyes.

A voice, easy and measured, with a hint of real amusement, spoke at my elbow. 'Do you know what you are trying to pound a hole into?'

The question seemed so daft that I looked up to see the comic. The speaker was leaning against the fence of the smallholding. Not a tall man, but beautifully made, broad shoulders, narrow hips. He had a well set, wide forehead, topped with hair that strayed a bit and curled. Bright blue eyes, sun-tanned skin, and strong white teeth in a mobile, sensitive mouth. He started to roll a cigarette with the ease of long practice and without even looking he ran his tongue along the paper's edge, parked his cigarette and lit it. I got the feeling of unhurriedness, of someone who savoured each moment.

'The ground, I suppose,' I replied somewhat sarcastically.

'Yes, that and more,' the stranger rejoined with a smile. 'You're folding over a Roman villa!' He thrust out a strong hand. 'I'm Roger Williams, this is my smallholding, such as it is.'

I told him my name and a friendship began that in a strange way was to change irrevocably the shape and pattern of my life. He bent down and picked up a rough cube of red bricklike material and placed it in my hand. 'There you are — a piece of tessellated pavement Romans walked on, back in the first century A.D.'

Hardly a day passed without us having a word. I would hurry back early after dinner to get the chance of a talk. Roger would take me for rambles over the Northchurch and Ashridge Commons in the evenings. At weekends we sometimes walked along Duncombe Terrace above Aldbury and out to the clean windswept contours of Incombe, then off again to Pitstone and back along the Tring Hills. Soon I was going along the road to Gossom's End on the edge of Berkhamsted. Mrs. Williams seemed to put up with my constant questioning of Roger and when time ran out, I would walk happily back to Northchurch, laden with books. What books they were, and what writing! A new world began to unfold and I was hungry and ready for it. For the first time I read W.H. Hudson's *Shepherd's Life*; Richard Jefferies' *The Story of My Heart*, *Field and Hedgerow*, *Bevis*, and *Nature near London*. I revelled in Henry Williamson's *Lone Swallows* and *Tarka the Otter*.

Roger showed me the world through the eyes of John Clare, A.E. Housman, Edward Thomas and Wordsworth. I grew to love them and often on Winter evenings, I would sit and listen to Roger reciting 'Into my heart an air that kills, from yon far country blows' or 'In Summertime on Bredon'. There was an underlying sadness and fatalism in Housman's poetry, which at that time appealed to my teenage sense of high drama.

I realised, too, that the only way to read poetry was to read it aloud, only then can it live, otherwise the poem is flat, a song without the music of the sound of words.

I have mentioned the forbearance of Kathleen, Roger's wife. She was always there and, of course, their three children: Anna, shy and quiet as a mouse, Ralph, not given to demonstration, and Mary, full of mischief and not backward in coming forward.

After rambles we would go back to Gossom's End and search through Coward's *British Birds* or Morris's *British Butterflies* and various guides to wild flowers. I learnt not only to see but to search, to produce the line, to go on asking questions and not to rest until I found the answer.

Roger suffered from asthma and between this great handicap and the rationing of animal foodstuffs his small-holding venture collapsed. For a little while Roger came to work on the farm. Between this and the cobbling he carried on from the front room of their cottage, his family managed to survive.

10. *Snowbunting*

Roger and I went many times on our bicycles to the Tring and Wilstone Reservoirs. My ancient binoculars were not designed for bird watching, especially over great expanses of water like Wilstone. We would lie there on the stone parapet, watching the Winter hordes of pochard and widgeon. Sometimes we counted as many as twenty grey heron, patient sentinels, unlike the restless redshanks, so quick to give their hysterical cries of 'pee-bee-be! pee-bee-be!' as they flung themselves into the sky, their wings flashing white-barred alarm signals.

One bitterly cold day in January 1944 we were bird watching at Wilstone. My hands were far too cold to hold my glasses. I was thinking about a hot cup of tea and a warm fire. Roger's hand moved very lightly on to my arm, he didn't speak but moved his head slightly. There, not a yard from us on the parapet, a snowbunting was perched. I don't know how long we watched this diminutive stranger from the snow lands, until just as suddenly it rose and let the cold wind take it away, a pale russet and white butterfly.

'Let's come next week, Roger,' I said eagerly, as we ground our way home against the wind.

'We'll see,' he puffed. 'Remember that in this game, you can come a hundred times and see nothing like that,' he said. 'But you must keep on coming.'

11. *Threshing Drum*

I first realised how ill Roger was when we were threshing over at Cold Harbour Farm. He was twenty-seven then, I was seventeen in the June of that year. We were late threshing the corn in the Dutch barn. In those days we had to wait for the threshing drum to come to us, we took our turn with many other farms.

Roger and I were working under the tin roof of the barn, there was little air anyway and wouldn't be until we got down below the eaves. The method was to open up a stand hole, in which a third man stood, whose job it was to keep supplied the man feeding the drum. Roger and I pitched sheaves down to the stand hole man. Obviously it was slow going at first, he had very little room to turn round in and any impatience on our part would get him 'right haggled up' as old Harry Durrant, the 'feeder' used to say.

I hated working under the sloping roof. There was no room to use our pitchforks properly and it soon became very hot, but the worst menace came from the dust. As soon as we started to move sheaves it started. In building a rick, whether in a barn or in the open, the dampest sheaves go on the top. This is good sense, it gives them a better chance to dry out without heating the rick, but these sheaves are the dustiest of all. Within minutes, Roger's face was grey as he fought for breath. I yelled to Harry Durrant and we got him out. After a while Roger went on the much heavier but much cleaner job of loading up the sacks of corn on the trailers.

I loved threshing days. The great steam engine drawing the thresher would lumber into the stackyard the night before and get squared up to the rick. The huge driving belts were eased into position, and the driver would check that the threshing was set level, or the belts could fly off. While the driver and his mate were engaged in that job, we would put small mesh nets round the rick to trap the rats.

Rats were not the only pests on the ricks, often at Cold Harbour I would walk round the back of the Dutch barn which faced the Oak Wood and see sixty or more grey squirrels move like a grey stream down the rick side and away into the safety of the trees.

When morning came everybody on the farm who could possibly be spared turned up. The driver and his mate saw to the technical side, Mr. Faulkner would come and watch the first sacks of corn off, checking the sample of corn coming through. The corn dropped down chutes at the end nearest the steam engine. 'Firsts' had two chutes, one bag filling and one empty, to give the corn man time to take the full bag off and put another empty in its place. There was a third chute for 'seconds', which filled more slowly and could therefore be easily changed when full, and a chute for weed seeds. When Mr. Faulkner had a good sample of corn, he would fill a couple of small canvas bags and go off to the corn exchange.

One man would knee the sacks of corn onto the scales, adding or taking away, until the weight was right. A corn bushel was stood alongside the scales to take the surplus corn. Yet another man wheeled the tied sacks to the waiting trailer and two men used a lifting stick to load up. My job at first was tying the sacks, not as easy as it sounds. The lip of the sack was turned outwards and downwards to form a collar and the rough twine wound round and tied tight. Corn sacks have to stand a lot of handling and bumping round and spilt corn is a cardinal sin.

At the other end the threshed straw was pushed out. In the case of wheat straw it would tumble into a straw trusser and the trusses would in turn be thrown onto an elevator and built into a stack; more usually it was stacked in an empty bay of a barn. This straw was in great demand for thatching the ricks. We had a stationary bailer which was used for barley and oat straw and stacking bales was much easier.

On the rick there would be perhaps three men and the key figure, the feeder, Harry Durrant. He stood by the hatch ready to feed the sheaves into the waiting maw of the drum. The last and dirtiest job was given to the youngest and most inexperienced member of the work force. The dustiest, dirtiest job imaginable. Large chaff sheets were laid out and the chaff (or kaff) was then scooped into a great heap, the corners of the sheet twisted, and the huge bundle hoisted over the shoulder, dragged away and dumped to be burned. Wheat chaff was saved and usually bagged up in chaff bags, it was good food for horses and cattle and not to be wasted.

Chaff, even when trapped in a great sheet, has a mind of its own as the unfortunate carrier soon finds out. It pours eagerly down the neck, finds its insidious way into the eyes and ears, by the end of the day your nose ceases to be a nose, your eyes are red smarting saucers. A sweep would pale into insignificance beside you. Barley was the arch enemy of the human ants that burrowed and sweated at the chaff hole. Someone said that it was rather like picking up vinegar with a fork. The barley awns worked and burrowed their spiteful way into every part of the body.

Steam was up, every man, woman and boy stood at his or her station. Harry Durrant stood atop the drum like a great conductor. He held no baton, but a razor sharp knife, the blade worn by years of honing. It was tied to his wrist by a loose leather thong (it wouldn't do to lose that in the drum), then raising his knife arm aloft, he would roar like thunder 'Set 'er away Tom.' Into gear went the complex giant; with a slapping of the great belts and a shuddering vibration, felt throughout the whole yard, the threshing drum awoke, stretched, flexed its myriad muscles and hummed and throbbed into magnificent life. Off went the pitchers, the lead man passing the sheaves ears first, to lie upon the raised apron in front of old Durrant. He would gather the sheaf, flick the knife hard into the band, gathering the tie in one movement. When he held a bunch of them, he would tuck them into his ample leather belt. The other hand and arm slid the corn into the drum. Durrant's ear could tell by the change in tone whether or not the drum was coping. On occasions he missed a sheaf — the drum would give a protesting 'whump' and the lads would yell 'Missed that un Harry' but that was pretty rare. It usually happened when we had a rough load coming through of sheaves and loose corn, due to some fault in the tying mechanism of the binder back in the harvest field.

12. *Sheep Again*

I was fresh from the 'smoke' as Edgar put it and the country scene was a source of continual wonder and joy to me. I learnt to contain myself in the presence of the old man, not that he was unkind or scathing about my green enthusiasm. On the contrary, as he accepted me as his lad, he began to talk more and more about the country lore he had learnt in years of shepherding. Edgar never talked at length but comments, brief, pertinent, packed with observation, studded our daylong companionship, like the small flowers of the rocks.

Sentiment never entered into it, he told what he saw and what he had learnt his observations to mean, in terms of living, nothing more.

We had snow in mid-March of that year, just a 'shatterin'' as Edgar called it. The sun shone the next day and I said cheerfully, 'That didn't come to much.' We were walking from the Home Farm across the common. Edgar jerked a thumb towards the frail stars that shivered in the keen wind upon the blackthorn 'We'da call that the blackthorn Winter. Look o'eer theer.' He nodded towards the high hills, capped white with a glistening birthday cake of snow. 'Mark my words, when t'snow lies on the hills it beckons for more.'

That night the wind dropped and with the falling barometer on the sheephouse wall, the snow began to fall again. Large flakes like torn white paper, swirled and danced in the headlights of the bailiff's car, spinning and sliding up the lane to the farmstead, as he returned from the village. I remember how that afternoon under a clear, windswept sky, Edgar had got me to carry out a bale of straw to spread under the lee of the basket hurdles in the fold. 'Lambs'll need a dry lie tonight I be thinkin'. I can smell snow a coming,' he said. The old shepherd read his daily weather forecast in the surrounding hills and woods, set in the context of changing light and wind. When Furzen Wood was black against the skyline, then rain was on the way, or if the sycamore in Dan East Wood showed the backs of their leaves, then it was time to reach for our raincoats.

One morning, eager to show my growing prowess in weather forecasting, I looked at the sky glowing red in the East and said confidently, 'Red sky in the morning, shepherd's warning — it'll rain soon.'

Edgar grinned at me, 'Think so young un?'

Half an hour later the sun had risen and the fire in the sky died back. A wind sprang up from the south-west and blew mild. 'No rain yet awhiles,' said the shepherd. Bang goes another weather saying I thought. The following day the same glowing sky greeted us before the rising sun. I said nothing. Ten minutes later Edgar said, with his grey head on one side, looking at me, 'Red sky in morning, shepherd's warning. We're in for a wet un.'

'But yesterday. . . .' I exclaimed.

'Ah, yesterday, that was different. Look at the sky now Davey.' The red banner had crept across the sky from the gateway of the East into the far West. 'Allus watch the clouds, if the fire dies back, then she'll be fine, but if like as now she reaches across the sky to the West, then rain'll coom.'

We spent most of that day as far as we could tidying up the caravan and making shackles. We could well afford to, for Edgar always tried to keep at least two folds ahead of the grazing sheep. Apart from giving us a respite in very wet weather, it meant that Sunday and Monday were easy days. We took it in turns on Saturday afternoons and Sundays, to go out to the fold, to trough feed and let the ewes on to the new fold. Then at teatime I'd go out to the field and rack up with hay. The big iron racks could be filled in the morning but the rib cages would get soaked if I filled them before night. Once when we were pitching a fold in the Summer near Heath Wood, the pheasants kept 'gock gocking' away. 'Thunder about,' said Edgar. 'Reckon they old birds can hear it rumbling miles away.'

In that part of Hertfordshire little owls were very numerous — most of the old ash trees had a resident. Edgar said that they always called when rain was about. He called them rain owls because of their 'wet wet' call, which always sounded rather ghostly and full of foreboding to me.

Another time when I was carrying hurdles for him to pitch, Edgar leant on his bar and said, as he looked at something on the ground, 'We be in for a spot I reckon, the little ole weatherglass has gone ter bed.'

I peered down and said very knowingly 'Oh, you mean the scarlet pimpernel.'

'Pimpernel me foot!' snorted Edgar, 'that be the poor man's weather glass. Little ole flower allus shuts up, when rains a'comin.'

As the lambing time finally dribbled to a halt and the last 'o' they cuckoo lambs' as Edgar contemptuously called them arrived on the scene, we began to spend a lot more time with the ewes and lambs at foot. I wondered at his scathing remarks about the handful of late arrivals in the yard. 'Tis like this,' said Edgar when I questioned him, 'these late uns miss the rush o' Spring, when everything is bustin' ter grow. They (he pointed with his crook at the leggy lambs) never really seem ter git away with it.'

13. *Sheephouse*

Given dry weather we were to begin tailing on Tuesday and on Monday afternoon I was sent up to the farm to get Billy the white pony and the light shepherd's float. Then I was to call at the Sheephouse to pick up the tailing board, the iron, and anything else Harry had a mind to give me. I soon had Billy harnessed up and went bowling down to the Sheephouse. This was a new shed of which Harry, the Head Shepherd, was very proud. It was built of wood — neatly weather-boarded along its length and the two ends. It was roofed with red tiles. The front stood open facing a green paddock, which was divided into large pens with chestnut paling. The shed itself had a floor of driven chalk and was divided into two large pens by a close rail fence. Two wooden troughs ran the length of this fence, one on either side. The rear wall was furnished with a hay rack which ran the length of the shed. Each pen contained about twenty young rams, some lying down, some pulling at the hay, and as always a few passing the idle hours by butting one another furiously.

At the far end there were two small pens. A thick wooden Y-shaped gadget, its stem rooted in the floor, stood in the centre of the space before the pens. I gathered from the hole bored in each arm that it was used as some kind of yoke. A cupboard with its door ajar hung on the side wall, and I glimpsed pairs of shears, strange instruments, and rows of bottles of all shapes and sizes.

The rest of the wall was covered with red, blue, yellow and white prize cards and gaily coloured be-ribboned rosettes from shows all over the country. I read names like 'Three Counties', 'Bath and West', 'The Royal', 'Great Yorkshire' and many of the other county shows.

Just inside Harry's sanctum stood a large tin drum, full of beans. They were the small brown field beans. I had often used them when rolling oats for the sheep up at the Home Farm. We used to put a handful in the hopper now and again. They were too 'soapy' to mill on their own but mixed in with the drier oats, their oil was absorbed and they didn't stick to the rollers. Anyway, beans or not they smelt to high heaven.

Footsteps sounded down the path from Harry's cottage and he swung round the corner of the shed. A tall, lean, muscular figure, fresh complexioned with blue eyes and lank black hair which kept dropping across his forehead. He wore collar and tie, neat blue overalls and heavy boots. 'Hallo, Davey, have you come for the tailing gear?'

'Yes, shepherd,' I answered.

'With you in a minute then, must have a "pee". Time for that even in harvest time.' He turned away and relieved himself in the drum of beans. I must have looked shocked for when he turned round he said, 'That's why I keep 'em in here, it helps the nitrogen content. Right now, tailing board.'

He lifted up a board mounted on four legs from behind him and placed it on the concrete paving. 'Tailing irons.' A bundle of what looked like children's sand spades made of iron, each with a wooden grip at the top, followed. 'Lambing oil and swab. Reckon that's about it,' said Harry. 'Oh, you had better fill up two sacks, maybe three, of logs from the pile at the end of the shed, for firing.'

I loaded up the float and was just about to pull away when Harry called 'Just a minute Davey, I was forgetting the fire stones. There's none down at Holly Bush. You can have four good flatties from here. I kept 'em from last year when we tailed in Cherry Orchard just over the hedge.'

We loaded up the stones and I jogged away round the Common to turn up the trail which led through the Beeches, along the top of Tunnel Field. A missel-thrush was singing from the top of a withered ash, throwing liquid phrases of song into the wind. No other song seemed to catch the spirit of early Spring, as his did.

'Bin a mort o' time lad,' grunted Edgar. 'Let's get un off an' then you best be gettin' Billy back to the farm an' loose 'im out. Then git off 'ome fer yer tea.'

14. *Tailing*

The morning jobs were got through double quick. It was bright and sunny. The wind had dropped and Edgar was delighted. 'Weather be perfect fer t'job,' he grinned.

The ewes and lambs were lying in the back fold. Edgar had cornered them and not let them on to the new fold. We had pitched two pens parallel to the outside net. Into the first of the pens we ran the flock. I went and opened the hurdles on to the fresh feed, then with Edgar standing at the hurdle between the pens, we let the ewes through into the further pen, holding the lambs back. Now and again a lamb slipped through and the process was held up until I had caught it. When we had a good number of ewes run off, we let them go to find their way up to the fold. The noise of ewes and lambs was deafening as they were separated, but gradually we sorted them all out and the lambs lay in the first pen. 'Put the last of the ewes out,' said Edgar, 'then fasten the hurdles.'

Many of the ewes hung back, reluctant to leave their bleating offspring but gradually they drew away to feed. Edgar sent me for a bale of straw and I spread this in the pen the ewes had left. 'Keep it near the sides,' called the old man, 'that's where the lambs'll lie.'

Whilst I did this, he set to making the fire. I had arranged the stones and in no time it was blazing merrily. 'Put on plenty of logs when she gets a good 'old,' said Edgar. 'I'll put the kettle on the stove, Harry'll wanna cup fer sure.' He brought the irons over before going to the shed and arranged them around, putting the ends deep into the fire.

We had just poured the tea when Harry put his head around the door. 'Reckon he smelt it,' laughed Edgar. They fell to talking — the subject was sheep.

'The lambs should do all right here,' said Harry. 'This field never had much "tetnus".'

'Ah,' replied Edgar, 'give us a nice dry spell an' they lambs'll git away nicely.'

'What's "tetnus"?' I asked.

'Why that's the fancy name for lockjaw,' said Harry. 'That's why I like burning tails off — the heat cauterizes and seals the wound like. That's the reason Edgar wants a dry spell — to give the tails time to dry. The knife is quick but they bleed too much, especially when they're big lambs.'

'Couldn't you tail them earlier?' I asked.

'Tell 'im Edgar,' laughed Harry.

'I've used the knife and me teeth at times,' said the old man. 'Tha's all right for little tackers, but we're breeding good "Down" stock 'ere. We be looking fer a good thick dock.' I must have looked mystified for Harry broke in, 'That's the stump of the tail. A good dock gives a ram or a ewe a nice finish behind. I always reckon that leaving 'em late helps to grow a better round leg o' mutton.'

Harry looked over the pen of lambs, 'We'll make a start, bring a couple of those old coats with you Davey, I'll set the tailing board up.'

We always kept a goodly selection of coats in the hut, for a wet day meant several changes. I grabbed two and jumped down the steps. 'All right for some,' grunted Edgar, and clambered down after me. Although he rarely talked of it, his arthritis was becoming increasingly painful.

Harry set the tailing board at right angles to the wire, handy to the fire, which we had lit midway between the two pens. 'Fetch me a spare hurdle Davey.' I ran to do his bidding. This hurdle he set up on end between the wire and the tailing board. 'Now hang the coats over it to form a back rest. How are the irons Edgar?'

'Jest right Harry, start when you're ready.'

Edgar sat astride the board and I caught the first lamb, lifting it over the hurdle to him. He held it against his body taking a fore and hind leg in each hand, so that the lamb sat upright, the tail along the board. Quickly Harry moved in, he spat on the iron to test the heat, then holding the tip of the tail brought the iron down with a quick yet easy movement on to the tail. Pungent smoke arose, the lamb kicked and gave a faint cry. The tail was flicked away and, reaching down, Harry came up with the swab, from the tin of lambing oil. Bleeding was almost completely absent and with a moment's glance he smeared the stump with lambing oil. Edgar swung the lamb round easily and dropped it into the strawed pen and I was ready with another.

Sometimes the iron was too quick and did not seal the wound, then Harry would stop the bleeding by applying the corner of the iron, remarking 'Iron just a shade hot, I'll draw 'em back from the fire a bit.' Generally the tail was off and the lamb away into the pen with little trouble. The tailed lambs in the pen seemed more concerned about joining their mothers than about their missing tails.

'There's another thing about this job,' said Harry. 'Long tails on folded sheep, especially Southdowns, 'ud mean a lot of trouble from blowfly. They git so dirty yer see, not like sheep on hard tack — like the Blackfaces, anyways they need their tails ter protect their udders from the frost at night.'

When we had tailed forty-odd lambs, we stopped for a moment. Harry cast an expert eye over them, just in case any were still bleeding, then we opened the hurdle and away they went to find their mothers, some of whom had already drawn back down the fold to seek their famished offspring. By dinnertime the job was done. My arms ached but I was pleased that I had caught all the lambs single-handed and that we hadn't had a slip. At Edgar's bidding I cleared up the straw in the standing pen and spread it along in the lee of the basket hurdles. 'If it wets ter night,' said Edgar, 'they'll be needing a dry lie.'

When I returned from this chore, Harry and Edgar were busy sorting the tails out into bundles of ten. I watched with interest. I had noticed that whenever I had asked Edgar how many lambs we had, he didn't know. At any rate he would shy off the subject. Harry looked up, 'Nigh on three hundred lambs, Edgar — a good lambin'.'

Edgar turned to me, 'Now ye know how many we got. Yer see no shepherd counts lambs 'til theer tailed. Do yer wanna bunch of tails fer yer lan'lady?'

'Tails?' I said in horror.

'Don't throw up yer hands,' laughed Harry. 'She'll welcome 'em, there's nought like lamb tail pie.'

I had my doubts. 'Anyway,' I said, 'how on earth do you get the wool off?'

'That be easy 'nuff,' said Edgar. 'Jest drop 'em inter a

pan o' boilin' water. Then you can plote 'em like a chicken.'

Finally persuaded, I took a bundle of fat lambs tails that night to my landlady. There was certainly no mistaking the look on her face, she was delighted, and knew all about ploting! Lamb's-tail pie was out of this world, with a tender, sweet, melt-in-your mouth quality. There would be no hesitation on my part next tailing.

15. *The Letter*

We settled down to the routine of folding again, moving slowly up and down the great field. The next job was castrating and ear-marking, to be done as soon as the effects of tailing had worn off. We lost one lamb with lockjaw; I saw it standing in the fold, its stump of a tail held at right angles. It was listless and droopy. Harry said that sometimes quick action with the knife could save a lamb, the tetanus organism being at first local and then gradually spreading through the nervous system, so that a speedy operation could remove the organism but in this case we were too late and the lamb 'went 'ome' as Edgar put it.

The old man was in one of his 'thinkin' moods' for some days. A longer one than usual, so that I began to think that his arthritis was troubling him more than a little. Then I noticed that Edgar kept stealing sideways glances at me as if weighing me up. 'What's wrong Edgar?' I said.

He started as if bitten. 'Wrong? What be arskin' me fer. I'll tell ye if owts wrong.'

I shut up, knowing the danger signs.

The next day, having a cup of tea, I felt his eyes on me again. Now and then his hand strayed to his jacket pocket, only to be snatched away again as if on a string. I ignored it all. Suddenly the old man said 'Do summat fer I, Davey?'

I turned and looked at him, 'You know without asking that Edgar.'

'S'pose I do at that,' he grunted. The hand strayed again to the pocket. This time the fingers came away clutching a grubby envelope. He thrust it towards me as if frightened that he might change his mind.

'Will ye read 'is fer me Davey?'. Edgar turned his eyes from me. 'Iver, iver fergart me glasses.'

I read the letter to Edgar. It wasn't very long and it was already three years old. Afterwards the old man folded it carefully, replaced it in the dog-eared envelope and carefully stowed it away in his jacket pocket. I never did see Edgar's glasses, and I made no comment. In all the time I was with him I only read four letters and Edgar never made the excuse about his glasses again.

The first letter I read for Edgar was three years old when the old man finally got round to asking me to read it for him. The postmark Salisbury, was only just discernible. Edgar later told me that he had left school at eight years old. 'Never did marster readin' an' writin'. I was a "looker" on the Downs 'bove Sarlsbry. I kin still 'ear them ship bells chimin' thro' the mist of a mornin'. Them wus good days ter be shepherdin'.'

16. *Invasion*

It happened without warning, not out of the blue, but out of the swirling grey mist of a March morning came tanks like monstrous squat toads. There must have been a dozen in line abreast, filling the air with the squeal of wheels and metallic clatter of treads. Two went smack through the sheep fold dragging the twisted nets after them, they were on it before they knew we were there. I remember Edgar cursing, stream after stream of imprecations as he stood waving his crook, hardly yet believing his eyes. The tanks rolled on, with infantrymen, khaki anonymous figures, looming up and disappearing in the wake of the tanks. They went crawling through Durrant's thorn hedge which he had almost finished laying. I saw Durrant almost weeping with rage, crying to a young smooth-faced officer, 'Why can't the buggers go through the one 'ole?' And the officer, nauseatingly cool, replying, 'I'm frightfully sorry, but the enemy would line up his guns in no time. Not to worry, the wiring parties are following up.'

'Aye but they can't put my 'edge back,' yelled Durrant, at his retreating back. They never did; months later oak posts and rail fences filled the gaps torn right across the farm. We were a couple of days sorting pigs, sheep and cattle out from all sorts of unlikely corners.

And over at Cold Harbour a young boy from the 'Devons' lay in the hayloft, shaking in high fever. A foretaste of the real pain to come to many.

17. *Castrating and Ear Marking*

I cannot say that I was looking forward to this job, but as Edgar said it was a job that had to be done; in any case because we were a ram breeding flock, we left a good percentage of the ram lambs entire. I asked Edgar how the job was done. 'Tis easy these days,' said Edgar. 'I mind the time when we der use the knife, but now Harry's got they 'Zealand pincers! They do's a proper job, no trouble.'

The next day at the sheep shed I asked Harry if I could see the 'Zealand pincers. 'I'll do more than that,' he said. 'I'll give you a demonstration so that you know just what's happening.' He went to the cupboard and drew out a flat cardboard box. 'Patent New Zealand Emasculators' it said. 'Take 'em out,' laughed Harry, 'and put 'em on the bench. I'll jest slip up home a second.'

I took them out, gleaming chrome pincers with the black handles set wide apart. The jaws curved round to meet each other in a blunt black line of metal. They looked fearsome. Harry reappeared carrying an envelope and a piece of string. 'Hold the castrators in your hands,' he said. 'That's it, open the handles.' I did so and the jaws moved apart. 'Now close them — slowly — until the jaws meet.' I pressed on and felt them move together. 'Now try to tighten still more,' said Harry. There was a clicking sound. 'That extra pressure does the trick,' he said. 'Watch this.' He took a piece of string and placed it lengthwise down the centre of the envelope, this he sealed. 'Right, open the castrators, hold one hand above the other, for that's the position you'll be in. Move the open jaws over the bottom of the envelope and up until they are over the centre of it.' I followed his instructions. 'Now close the jaws as before and try to move the envelope.' I tried but the jaws were gripping firmly. 'All right Davey, squeeze.' I squeezed and felt the handles move together with a click. 'Open up and move 'em away,' smiled Harry. We opened the envelope and Harry showed me how the string inside had been neatly severed although the envelope itself was unmarked.

'Nothing in it,' he said. 'All we do is to sever the cord so that no sperm can travel from the testicle and in time they will atrophy, that is, die back, no external wound is caused and this cuts out the risk of infection. The only difficulty is that with a smallish lamb, using this method there is a risk of rupturing them. That's why we like the ram lambs well grown, apart from the fact that it gives us more chance to see what they will grow into.'

Two days later, the fine spell came and we set about the job using the same system of sorting that we had done for tailing.

I realised now that the paint numbers carried by the ewes and given to their respective lambs had far more significance than I had realised. It was not just an aid to the shepherd, in picking out which lamb belonged to which ewe. Now each lamb was to receive a number — a tattooed number in the ear — giving flock, year and dam. The shepherd had to know, in the case of foster lambs, that the ewe mothering them was not the dam. He could also tell by going back in his records the numbers of twins or singles dropped by an individual ewe each year she was in the breeding flock; and also the sire of her lambs, though this was established in a different way at mating. I had this first year the job of putting the letters and numbers into the tattooing pliers. These were made of sharp needles of metal set into a base which slotted into the top lip of the pliers.

The ear was taken between the jaws of the pliers. The tattooing needles locking down as it were, on the inside of the lamb's ear, which was liberally daubed with tattooing ink. The bottom half of the ear received the number and care had to be exercised so that the small arteries traversing the ear were not punctured, otherwise the tattooing ink would spread along these, producing a bloom of tattoo which could render the number unreadable. The pliers were spring-loaded and in theory at any rate sprang back to the open position when the pressure was released. Sometimes they didn't and then the man holding the lamb had to hold it very still, so that the ear was not torn.

The breed number went into each right ear — Harry said that some breeders did not mark the individual ewes. The flock number only went into the left ear, so that I had two pairs of tattooing pliers on the go.

Stan from the farm staff joined us on this day. He caught the lambs and shouted 'ewe' or 'ram'. Edgar sat astride the tailing board and held the lambs, whilst Harry castrated and tattooed.

I was on hand changing the tattooing letters and numbers and sometimes lifting the lambs back over for Edgar, for they were by now quite a weight. It wasn't a rush job. Futures — sheep futures — were being decided, certainly in the case of tne ram lambs. 'Ram lamb' Stan would shout and Edgar would fight for a minute to pin down the waving legs, then control won would say 'Waddyer think Harry?'

Harry, tugging his chin, 'Well made un Edgar. Good colour legs and nose. Well woolled on top — wool to the ear tips. I like him — got the makings of a good tup. Tattoo Davey. . .' and a big bony hand would reach back to me.

Sometimes the verdict was different. 'Don't reckon much to this un Harry.'

'No, Edgar, he'll never make much, I'll cut him.' The operation was quick and expertly done and the ram lamb — now a wether — was dropped quickly into the fold. They walked stiffly for a while, but a day or two later seemed none the worse.

The job done we cleared up. Edgar and I walked through the re-united flock. We had marked the wethers with a red shoulder dot, for we would need to check these in a fortnight or so, to see whether or not the scrotum was shrivelling, the sign that the operation had been properly performed.

18. *Sheep Faces*

I had learnt a lot about conformation and type and had begun to be able to pick out in our breeding flock of two hundred and fifty, ewes that had been brought in from other flocks. Before coming to the farm, sheep had just been sheep to me, nothing more. Now I was beginning to pick out the different breeds; black-faced, clean-legged Suffolk, the rangier, tan-faced Clun, the attractive Kerry Hills with their bright black and white faces and legs.

Edgar took me yet another stage and began patiently to teach me to pick out different strains within our own breed of Southdowns. He would stand hunched over his crook surveying the flock, now and again raising his arm to point out a particular ewe. 'That ewe near the trow end Davey, she be a Gaddesden ewe, look at the length of body, I like they.' His bright rheumy eyes moved away, 'Now that ewe — she be out of the Luton Hoo type, rare colour and a grand body. Sumthin' like a Southdown she be. Over there now, those two feeding close. They be Langmeads, I reckon they've swept the board for long enuff at the shows.'

All two hundred and fifty ewes were individuals to Edgar and he and Harry were working all the time to produce a strain of their own, combining all the good features, in wool and conformation.

'Funny thing Davey, the best show sheep ain't the best field sheep by a long ways. 'appen we lose t'motherin' side — yer know, the art'er lambin' and milkin' like — 'cos we tries too 'ard fer other things. I seen long 'eaded rangy ewes yer wouldna give 'ouse room to, lamb easy as yer like, bring up thumpin' great twins, wi' ample milk, an' make toppin' mothers. Allus remember lad, there's more ter breedin' than yer can see wi' yer eye.'

19. *The Crook*

Early May came in with a rush of sun and blossom. Walking abroad was to walk in a long garden that had no boundary fence. Sky mixed with earth to float in clouds of pink and white May blossom on the thorn and slipped beneath the awning of the wood, to lie in pools of bluebell shimmering. Tunnel Field was crowned once more with a cathedral nave of beeches in their glory, which led to the chancel peace of the Hollow, where the nightingales were choristers in chief.

It was a time of hot sun and sudden heavy showers. I sat with Edgar in the hut, listening to the rain drumming on the tin roof. The ewes and lambs had drawn over into the shelter of the tall thorn hedge.

'Jest wait till this lot is finished,' grunted Edgar, 'they green bottle flies'll be thick as jewels on the sheep.'

The rain stopped just as if someone had turned the tap off. 'Roight,' said the old man. 'Ye take the crook. I'll bring the shears and the "salve".' He reached for the bottle of diluted Jeyes fluid — a lemonade bottle with a loop of string for carrying and a pierced cork in the top, then stuck the leather guarded shears into his belt. Slowly he clambered down the steps, collecting his twisted old thorn stick at the bottom; his arthritis seemed to make each day more difficult.

The sun was bright again in the fold, with an intensity of light that made one screw up the eyes. Steam rose from the sheep and brought the sharp tang of the sheep fold to us. We walked together through the flock, suddenly Edgar pointed to a ewe. 'Catch 'er.' I made a lunge with the crook, missed by a mile and made another desperate effort to catch her, sending the sheep and lambs skeltering in all directions. 'Wert!' roared Edgar. 'Stop darting about loike one o' they blue-arsed flize and larn ter walk soft in the fold!' I stood and waited for him to come up to me. 'Na then, what 'ave I told 'e abaht using the crook.'

Red-faced and penitent I repeated the time-worn formula 'Never try to hook a sheep. Let it run into the crook neat and sweet. Turn the crook and walk down the handle

54

to your sheep and hold it.' Edgar grinned delightedly 'Yer see, yer know. Na go an' do it!'

The next time he pointed out a ewe, I caught it quietly and with no trouble. I turned the crook so that the curl turned up and behind the joint of the leg, locking the ewe in. Then I moved my hands down the wet warm shaft and held the ewe. 'Good lad, that's more loike it. Now turn 'er and hold 'er fer me.' I put my left arm under the ewe's chin, bringing my hand up and round to hold her, then with my right hand gripped the flank away from me. Using my right knee as a pivot I swung her over and let her drop down gently on her side. Edgar moved towards me, planted his thorn stick firmly in the soft earth and began to walk down it, hand over hand. I could guess the pain this caused him by the sweat standing out on his forehead and his short intakes of breath. I waited, saying nothing. I knew that it was useless to try to help him. Edgar was a proud man and I had yet to see him give in to pain.

Once on his knees the old man started to cut away the soiled wool with his shears, revealing a patch of maggots covering an area about the size of a half crown. He flicked these off with the back of the shears, then gave a liberal dowsing of salve, starting at the edge of the shorn area and working to the centre, explaining as he did so 'Remember Davey, the moment the shears touch the maggots, they start a'moving' out into the fleece. That's why I cuts away back from the strike.' He saw the puzzlement on my face, 'Strike — that's where the fly first lay her eggs. Another thing, as the maggots work into the sheep they make a juice, which soils the wool, and this attracts more of the green bottle flies.'

We caught two or three lambs that had been scratching their necks with muddy hind feet and the green bottle flies had been attracted to the wet soiled wool. Edgar dealt with these in a different manner; he fumbled in his waistcoat pocket and brought out a penny with which he proceeded to rub out the tiny maggots. 'Why do you do that, Edgar?' I asked.

'There's nowt ter clip away on the lambs, an' the touch of copper is death to they maggots. I allus carry a penny.'

We continued on our way, backwards and forwards through the flock. Edgar's eyes were never still but all the while he scanned his sheep.

'Why did you say that this weather was worse for fly, Edgar?' I asked, as I let a ewe go loose and we got to our feet.

'Well, Davey, wet warm wool is just the place for the fly to strike. Most times they go fer a dirty sheep or lamb — that's why we dags 'em — clean 'em up behind in the Spring, the ewes that is.'

'How can you so quickly spot the sheep that are struck, Edgar?'

'Practice,' said the old man. 'Look at that ewe over in the corner with her head hung down. She's struck bad — watch now! See how she shakes her head and stamps her feet.'

I caught the ewe and we attended to her. She must have had a dozen strikes on the neck and down over the shoulders.

'They be like folks,' said Edgar. 'When they're hurt real bad, they jest wants ter creep away an' hide thersels. This ewe'd be a gonna in three or four days, if she were running on the Common, she'd run into the bracken and wait for death.'

We had to dress the ewe's raw places with an evil smelling ointment concocted by Edgar. 'This'll keep off the black fly and give it a chance to 'eal loike.'

'Black fly? I thought it was the green bottle fly that caused the trouble, Edgar.'

'That be roight young un,' he answered. 'They do make the strike but once the flesh is broken then the black fly — little biting tackers — move in. It's same at shearin' if ye cuts a ewe — there's no end o' trouble if the black fly starts feeding in it. They seem to like a dry open wound.'

20. *Birds of the Fold*

Before leaving the smoke of Sheffield, my bird watching had been confined very largely to the museum on wet Saturday afternoons. Now I realised just how much I had absorbed and was able to recognise immediately many of the birds that visited the fold. Edgar's names for them were far more colourful and descriptive than mine, and I quickly learnt the country names: Peggy dishwasher as opposed to pied wagtail, bottle tit for long-tailed tit, and so on. His eyes were as keen as a hawk's and as we pitched hurdles or sat having our 'bait' on the pile of hay bales, he would draw my attention to different call notes or just point to something happening.

Wild creatures seemed to accept us as part of the scenery, as harmless as the sheep we tended. This often gave us a grandstand view of the drama being played out around us.

I used to sit with Edgar and enjoy the company of perhaps a dozen bluetits busily clearing up the corn scattered around the bin. When we were folding near the woods, a nuthatch would dart down, seize a grain of corn and fly off to fit it into a crevice of a nearby tree, there to hammer it into submission. They were the picture of smartness — grey slate upper plumage, black eye streak and warm buff throat shading to rich chestnut on the flanks. One grew so trusting that it would take corn from the bale at Edgar's side providing that we kept perfectly still.

The laughter of the great green woodpecker often rang across those dry, green Chiltern valleys. Edgar would say 'Hark ter the yaffle — there's rain about.' We would watch its dipping flight carry it out of sight. One misty morning there was a clatter of wings as a crowd of starlings threw themselves into a bramble patch — panic stations! Edgar touched my arm, 'Look,' he breathed. A sparrow hawk lifted like a grey javelin over the hedge and sped towards the sheep troughs. A hedge sparrow still hopped unconcernedly between them. Suddenly it saw the hawk and with a squeak of terror hurled itself towards the safety of the trough. We saw the sparrow hawk move like a bullet, its wings lifting as it shot out yellow-legged talons. Feathers flew into the air. 'He's had it, Edgar,' I said.

'No,' said the old man. 'Look at the old 'awk na!' The sparrow hawk was hopping up and down the line of troughs peering under and round them, cold fury in his savage yellow-rimmed eyes. At length he gave up and beat away across the field. A minute later a tail-less hedge sparrow flew uncertainly, like a large brown bumble bee, to the greater safety of the hedgerow.

One January I remember Edgar saying quite casually, 'They birds be on the arzy bushes agin this mornin'. Seed 'em yesterday, 'bout same place.'

'What birds?' I asked.

'Dunno that I rightly knowed 'em.' The old man scratched his head reflectively. 'They be starlin' size er there 'bouts, brownie with peaky heads to 'em. Fair bit of yellow round the tail end — wi' summat o' red on their wings. I jest stood awhile lookin' an' they took no fright at I.'

'Waxwings, Edgar,' I cried excitedly. 'Can I go and look? I've never seen them before.'

Egar smiled 'Thought y'd be interested like. S'pose ye could slip up ter the sheep 'ouse an' fetch I some salt licks. Righto, off ye cut but dona be too long aways.'

So it was that for almost a quarter of an hour I feasted my eyes on the handsome visitors feeding upon the bright hawthorn berries. Edgar was right, they were tame and I was glad that it was very unlikely that any fool with an air-gun would spot them in that quiet corner of the Common.

I became quite proficient at imitating the cuckoo — not only the familiar 'cuckoo' of the male, but also the throaty bubbling note of the brown barred female. One afternoon a cuckoo flew over the fold, pursued hotly by two meadow pipits. It was a forgivable mistake, for no bird other than a hawk, looks more hawklike in flight. I called to it and it circled to the sound. This was not unusual in itself, but this male came right over us. I changed to the throaty broken cry of the female cuckoo and to my astonishment the cuckoo alighted within six feet of where I was pitching a net. Edgar and I watched almost unbelievingly as it began to display, fanning its tail and ruffling up its wings as it shuffled upon the ground. In the end I just burst out laughing and the cuckoo was up and away, looking, if a cuckoo can, very disgusted.

Edgar had the last laugh. 'Ye can say nuthin' na when I calls ye a proper cuckoo Davey!' and he laughed till the tears came.

Every day brought its crop of incidents to enliven the quiet hours, each deepening the sense of oneness with this world of the sheep folds; the funniest being when Edgar, peering round a haystock we were cutting into trusses for the sheep, looking for the hay needle we had lost, poked his hand into a hole and had fourteen Jenny wrens explode into his face — no doubt as surprised as he at being disturbed in their snuggery.

21. *Weaning*

We used to spein or wean the lambs at fourteen weeks or so, this was usually in mid-May. Obviously the ages of the lambs varied, some of the lambs being several weeks older, but it was more practical to wean the ewes and lambs in two main groups. The later lambs and the poorest of the twin lambs, were kept back until the second draft.

The ewes were put out to poor pasture in order to help them to dry off — lose their milk — as quickly as possible. We still had to keep a close watch upon them, in case any ewes developed trouble in the udder through still making milk. This was not so difficult as we had to make a complete check on their feet at this time and this, of course, necessitated catching and turning each ewe. We also drenched the ewes to clear away worm infestation, this had had to be avoided whilst the ewes were feeding their lambs, as the milk could be affected by the drench.

The lambs soon settled down to life on their own. It was usual for them to lose some weight at first, though this was hardly noticeable in the older lambs. Once they had 'got away' as Edgar put it, we drenched them also for worms, but at all times we were at pains to avoid exposing them to double shocks. This meant double handling and perhaps might have seemed a time-wasting way of going about things, but I learnt to accept Edgar's golden rule that the sheep came first.

22. *Drenching*

We had penned the ewes in an old stockyard in the field we called Dan East's. A dark wood lay along the top boundary. Dan East's Wood, so named according to the tale, because long years before, a man driven out of his mind by unemployment and destitution had hanged his two small children from a sycamore. It was always a twig-snapping, nerve-jumping place of darkness and dank undergrowth.

The worm drench was mixed in a large bucket and it was my job to fill the small slender-necked drenching bottles and hand them to Edgar as needed. It was a monotonous job. With one eye I watched the old man as he drenched a ewe and then pushed it out into the yard. I passed him another bottle, and another, and another. . . A kestrel sailed out of a far ash tree, to hang hovering over the pasture, tail fanned and wings splayed. I watched. . . 'Davey, what be gawpin' at na. I've asked 'ee nigh on six times for a bottle.'

Edgar released the ewe he was struggling with. 'Roight! Na ye kin try 'un yersel. Coom on.'

We changed places and Edgar stood with bottle poised, waiting. I caught a ewe and suddenly realised that although I had watched Edgar catch dozens of ewes, I had no idea of how to hold them, still less how to get the bottle into the ewe's mouth.

'If ye hadna bin watchin' that fool bird, ye might have larnt summat,' scolded Edgar. 'Na then, get astride the ewe, or pin her with yer knee agin the 'urdles. Yer left 'anded, so put yer right arm down her right side under her chin and round. That's it, na put yer four fingers into the back of 'er mouth and hold it open.' I did so and he handed me a bottle of drench. 'Roight, na put the bottle into the back of 'er mouth over yer fingers. Mind na, kip the bottle mouth pressed agin the roof of 'er mouth and tip it. Let the drench run down the back as it were.' The drench disappeared rapidly. I could feel the ewe swallowing. 'Let un go,' said Edgar, 'an' ketch the next.'

I drenched every one after that, quickly learning that unless the bottle found the top of the ewe's mouth, her tongue got in the way, and she either spat it out or choked violently.

'Iva seen ewes choked ter death in seconds, Davey. Allus make sure the bottle's in right before ya start pourin' it, an' give 'em time ter swaller, an' ye'll be all right.'

23. *Badgers*

When the ewes were grazing on open pasture, it was our custom to tie nets to the existing fence or just drive in a stake or two to hold the net back against the rough hedge. We always used old nets for this job whenever possible. One Spring morning we were walking the boundary fence of such a field — looking to see just where we would need nets. A good thickset hedge was normally sheep-proof, but many of the old thorn hedges had 'run away'. This means that the hedge had been allowed to grow too tall and the hawthorns had developed thick stools — trunks in miniature. All the new growth was at the top and the dead branches and twigs at the bottom stood no chance in holding back the pushing, questing sheep. When this happens the hedge is said to have no 'bottom'.

We noted the places and worked out the various nets we would need. Suddenly Edgar bent down by an old stile which led into Stony Bottom, now called Christmas Tree Valley by the children, since the plantation of spruce and larch had grown up. The shepherd beckoned me, 'Look 'ee here Davey, tis old Brock.' I bent closer and along the bottom rail I could see black and grey hairs. 'I 'specs she'll 'ave 'er cubs out be na,' said Edgar.

'Do you know where the sett is, Edgar?' I asked.

He turned towards the field and pointed 'See that girt sycamore?' I nodded. 'It stands in a big dell 'ole. 'er sett be

61

unner it. Ider see grass'n bracken she der throw out arter the long sleep.' Edgar rested his back against the stile and continued, 'I likes 'em. Never did see any 'arm in 'em. They gotta live same as we. Las' Summer ole George — gamekeeper chap — wanna know if I'der seen 'em. "They badgers be a rollin' the corn flat, 'sides takin' my eggs 'ee sez." But I jest looks right simple an' knows nuthin'.' He chewed a bit of grass reflectively. 'I mind once over seein' 'em digga sett. They der cum for ole Brock wi'd pincers and yelping dawgs. No kinda sport fer me. I der got more room for redcoats and 'osses an' all, than that goin' on. Mind me Davey, an' say nuthin'. Go an' look an' larn but say nuthin', tis better so.'

I remember going to the sett by moonlight, close-wrapped in an old greatcoat to sit for what seemed to be hours. Often I saw the badgers poking their white striped heads out of the sett, then lumbering over·to rub themselves on the worn stump of an elder. Later I watched two badgers cubs playing with a white object. The next morning I went down into the dell hole and found a young badger's skull, white, clean and with teeth that rattled. The crown of the skull fascinated me with its high thick ridge, bone which ran from nape to crown, giving a clue to the amazing strength of the badger's skull.

Once I inadvertently walked between an adventuring young badger cub and the sett, and watched laughing as it careered back on stumpy legs, grunting in distress.

24. George Berry — Pigman

I spent six months on the pig farm at Cold Harbour, working with George Berry. He wasn't easy to get to know. Slow of speech and taciturn, old facial injuries received on the Somme gave the impression that he was always about to smile. The scars were white now, the hurts of a yesterday he would never talk about. George never laughed at my ineptness, but slowly and easily, with few words, showed me how to do the different jobs.

I was very nervous about entering the pens with the

enormous large white sows and their pink shrill-voiced litters. 'You do right,' said George. 'When a sow bites, she hangs on, clamps her jaws and crushes. It pays to respect them.' I followed him into a pen, the sow came out with her piglets skittering around her. She was long, white and hairy, catching my scent she bridled away from us and opening her mouth 'yarred', showing great yellow teeth. As she turned for a closer look with a distinctly nasty expression in her cold hard eyes, I moved closer to George.

'Watch,' he breathed. He began to talk to the sow in soft crooning tones, moving nearer to her all the while. Slowly his hand reached out and he began to stroke the long back. The yellow wirelike bristles were lowered, the sow already looked several sizes smaller. Within minutes she was lying on her side, sighing with contentment, and the piglets, never slow to miss a chance, were lined up at the milk bar.

George moved away with me and showed me how to change her bed. 'If you really want to make a pigman, then there's one thing you must learn to do.'

'What's that?' I was eager to learn.

'Learn to think like a pig!' I thought George was pulling my leg. 'Aye, think like a pig,' he repeated almost to himself. 'You see this piggery. It was designed by the Architect as a palace for pigs. Well, palaces aren't the most comfortable of places to live in, great draughty places mostly. Look at these pens, they're all alike. Dung passage, sleeping quarters, and yard outside. Pigs by nature are clean animals, they like a separate toilet, so that the sleeping quarters are kept clean and dry. Naturally they sleep on the highest bit of ground available and keep muck and wet in the lower. Now see here, the "master mind" who built this wanted a gradual fall from the back to the front. Good sense, but not pig sense; the highest ground here is the dung passage. Mind you, my pigs don't know that. When we first used this piggery the sows kept taking their bedding into the dung passage and using the bedroom for the toilet. Ignorant pigs?'

'What did you do about it, George?'

He moved more of the bedding away. 'Look here.' There, below the untidy heap, lay a five-bar gate, with old

basket hurdles laid across it. 'I just made the beds higher than the dung passage and then, because pigs don't like draughts, any more than we do, I used old hurdles to make a lean-to false roof over the sleeping place and threw some battens or trusses of straw on top. Pigs must be warm and snug, else they're miserable and unless animals be happy they won't do.'

Later that Summer we had a student helping us out. Perhaps it was our fault but we omitted to tell him that Sally, the big wild sow, had a litter in the Oak Wood. Sally always made her bed under a great holly bush and farrowed on her own. Nobody was allowed near, until her piglets were up and running about. This day one of Sally's piglets had strayed through a hole in the pig netting. Piglet like, it couldn't find the way back again. Frank, the student, ever helpful, caught the little one after a struggle and carried it squealing and hollering over to the fence. Frank never reached the fence, a massive shape, jaws agape, sailed over the netting and sent him flying. Then Sally was on him, 'yarring' and tearing. She gripped him across one thigh and hung on. We heard his screams from the bottom of the cider orchard. I reckon we would have heard him at Northchurch village! It took two of us and a four tine muck fork breaking across her snout and back to make her let go. Frank was lucky. Sally was old and her fangs likewise. His corduroy trousers no doubt helped, but he was terribly bruised and shocked.

Beyond the great Dutch barn that stood on the West side of the stock yard, lay Oak Wood. Within the wood a water tower poked its rectangular head into the tree tops. It became a favourite spot for me to visit, when I had my lunch break. The green primrose-breasted wood-warblers loved the wood and from my vantage point I could look down upon them, as with wings and tail fanned out, they parachuted earthward, calling 'see-see-see' as sweetly as only wood-warblers can.

Grey squirrels came in their dozens to raid the unthreshed corn stacks in the great barn. I often counted as many as sixty moving like grey rats up the rick side. Once I got to Cold Harbour at four o'clock in the morning. It was late April and nobody was astir. George Berry would have thought I had gone mad if he had seen me. I climbed the ladder of the water tower and sat waiting for the Dawn Chorus. The sun had not yet risen above the misty aisles of beech and coppices of silver birch. Grey mist wrapped tree branches round and dripped from the spider webs which festooned green gorse and the barbed wire entanglements of angry bramble.

A robin sang somewhere on the Common, splinters of song thrown into the half light. A great-tit, never one for half measures, struck his anvil and 'Peecher', 'Peecher' rang through the Oak Wood. From the round of pine trees above the Brickyard, a missel-thrush perched in the topmost bough, threw down the gauntlet of his song. The storms of the young year had long since blown themselves out, but it was as if he remembered and triumphed in this moment.

A blackbird flew to sing from the black barn ridge. His phrases were given easily, sweet full rounded notes which brought a sense of lazy unhurriedness, as if both singer and listener had all the time in the world to taste this present beauty. From behind me in the lightening wood came the reasonant drum roll of a great spotted woodpecker, and the 'ploy-ploy-ploy' of nuthatches. As if I were invisible a wren sat feather fluffed upon the water tanks and poured forth his waterfalls of song.

The sun was rising to give saffron crowns to the oak trees and as it caught the silken hammocks of spiders each gorse was decked with blue flowers.

A golden mist now hung about the green grace of silver birches and willow-warblers crowned the glory of morning with their cadences of song. All birds were singing now, lifting their voices to the sun, their sweetness far and near all undergirded by the slumbrous calls of wood-pigeons and the spring song of turtle doves. The chorus faded from me, moving onward over England with the rising sun and I came down to earth, to satisfy the hunger of the pigs, whose screams grew deafening at my approach to the sties. Once fed, the ear-splitting yells of the pigs subsided into frantic 'golloppings' and I was left to reflect, as I pushed the now empty meal barrows back to the mealhouse, upon the mystery and miracle of the Dawn Chorus.

25. *Foot-rotting*

Every shepherd is supposed to carry a knife, a piece of string and a shilling in his pockets, so the saying goes. I never did fathom the significance of the shilling, unless it was a reference to hiring money, paid by the farmer when he engaged the new shepherd at Michaelmas at the old hiring fairs. Edgar told me that in those days he wore a smock, carried his best crook and wore a lock of plaited wool in the band of his hat. I always felt that the coin mentioned should have been a penny, having seen the good use to which Edgar put his when maggotting.

My first knife was given to me by Edgar. 'Tis a Cooper's Real Lamb Foot Knife,' he said. 'So mind ye look arter it.' He had fished it out of the cupboard in the old hut one morning as we sat having our breakfast. The knife had one blade about three inches long, the back edge turned about an inch from its tip and ran down to meet the cutting edge in a point. Edgar turned his own out and laid it on the table — it was identical. 'No better knife fer the job. Reckon it were a sheep man as made 'em.' He fumbled in his waistcoat pocket and brought out a small flat tin, which he flicked open. It contained a black oil stone. Edgar held it between finger and thumb and began to sharpen his knife. 'Allus keep a good edge on yer knife Davey. Ye'll see why when we tackle them ewes this mornin'!'

We took the flock over to the dipping pens. These were a well designed range of pens, provided with swing gates for sorting the sheep and, built upon a concrete base, kept the ewes drier and cleaner. The dip itself was covered over whilst not in use — a very necessary precaution, with children about from the farm cottages, apart from the fact that if left open it soon became filled with blown leaves and other debris.

'Owd Bob' the Border collie worked with us, he took a delight in his work with the flock. If anything he was too

fast and Edgar had to give him the rough edge of his tongue.
'Not enough work for 'ee with a folded flock,' said Edgar.
' 'ee be too varst fer sense.'

Soon the ewes were penned. We let half run free again
to graze in the Home Meadow, there being no point in
keeping them all penned for a long time. 'They'll only
muck pens up,' growled Edgar.

We tackled the ewes a dozen at a time, working in a
small pen, so that they were easier to catch. Each sheep
had to be caught and turned. Edgar showed me how to do
this so that the ewes sat up on their hind quarters. 'I takes
the woight agin me legs, so she's a "lying" back. Not plumb
upright else she's a' sittin' on 'er dock — that's 'er tail end
— an' she'll struggle.' He showed me the wrong way and
the ewe kicked and heaved in protest. 'That's no gud yer
see. Na watch!' Edgar let the ewe slip just slightly to one
side and she sat quietly and comfortably without a movement.

'Na fer the feet. I does the front two, then the back 'un
that's not tucked un'er 'er. Then I lets 'er lie on t'other
side and do that back 'un. The less ye move yer ship the
better fer ye both.'

I watched him do the first dozen ewes. It was a slow
painstaking business. Each foot was first scraped clean.
They were not too dirty with the flock having been on the
pastures for some ten days. The ewes' feet I realised later
on were a comment upon the shepherd in charge. Often
the hooves merely needed trimming to shape and without
further treatment the ewe was released into the larger pen
to stand.

In that first dozen perhaps three were in need of drastic
treatment; each of these had hooves that were twisted and
distorted, and more often than not the first paring strokes
of the knife revealed rottenness.

'Tha's why they grows all twisted up like,' said Edgar.
'The hoof is not growing and wearing even. Like when we
be lame we carries that foot. An' ship traipsing about a
muddy fold git soft in the hoof — more chance fer rot ter
set in.'

The speed of his hand was incredible, the blade moved

unerringly whipping away the twisted shell.

Edgar stopped. 'Look 'ere Davey.' I peered at the hoof, not pleasant at all! He pointed with the tip of his knife. 'See that red line?' Beneath the white of young growth I could faintly see it, running towards the toe of hoof. 'Yes, Edgar.'

'That be the toe vein. When yer parin' ship's feet ye musna cut that. Never go too deep, use yer knife like ye was parin' cheese, till yer sees it. Then yer knows where ye are. An' use the back of the hoof ter git yer line.' He cleaned away the rotten hoof, then pointed to a tin hanging from the fence. 'Pass the ointment.' The ointment in question was dark green and tacky. This he applied to the hoof, finished off by drawing the stick with a dap of ointment through the cleft of the foot. 'She'll do,' grunted Edgar and he pushed the ewe onto her feet. 'Ye can 'ave a smoke fer a minute. I'll rest me back.'

We sat under the maples that overhung one corner of the pen and savoured the morning. 'What's the ointment made of Edgar?' I asked.

The old man looked at me from under his bushy eyebrows. 'Tis me own remedy. One day I'll be tellin' 'ee Davey, if ye goes on shapin' ter make a sheepman.' He looked across the shining grass to the blue woods of Ashridge. 'Tell ye one thing lad, that there ointment helps ter grow a good hoof, firm yer see, but ye can shape it wi' a knife. Some likes ter use liquid dressing an' they runs 'em through the foot-rot bath. Ider done it mesel' when ewes are heavy in lamb to save turnin' 'em, but I doan' like it. Reckon it makes the foot too hard — flinty almost, more an' that, it ken lock the foot-rot in an' that be worse.'

'Owd Bob' lay watching us, his amber eyes never leaving Edgar's face. 'That there dawg'll never be a patch on Nell but she be goin' blind and taint fair to work 'er ower much na. I seed 'er trottin' over t'Cold Harbour after the bailiff's hoss, this mornin'. She be a faithful owd bitch.'

We rose and set to work again. Now we both caught and foot-rotted. Once Edgar caught me reaching for the ointment. 'Wert,' he scolded. 'Taint no use puttin' balm on till ye've got the rottenness out. Doana be feared t'make 'em bleed, 'tis cleansing.'

Each pen of fresh ewes we brought in Edgar would survey with a critical eye. 'Ketch ee,' he would say, usually leaving me the easiest ewes, only now and again letting me tackle a bad one!

He pointed out a ewe which kept shaking a fore foot. 'We'll have that 'un an' I'll show 'ee summat.' I caught and turned her up. The foot which was annoying her looked sound at first glance, though I noticed that one hoof had a peculiar rounded appearance on the sole.

Edgar tapped it with the butt of his knife. It sounded hollow and the ewe jumped. Then Edgar pointed to a hole up on the side of the hoof. With quick sure strokes he removed the sole of the hoof. I started back in disgust, as Edgar shook and flicked the maggots out. 'Na look.' I peered at the foot, the maggots had gone deep but the flesh was pink and clean. 'Ole greenbottle fly 'as done us a good turn. Pass the ointment.' As he put the ointment on he continued 'Sometimes Iver done that mesel'. Gotta ewe with a terrible bad foot and I've put a shoe on and put a couple of maggots in. Not as cruel as seein' a ewe creep around wi' a rotten foot.'

I had seen the 'shoes' he mentioned, little canvas boots with a leather sole hanging in the shepherd's hut. 'What causes the rot Edgar?'

He scratched his stubbly chin. 'Now yer arskin'. Take Cherry Orchard now. Last year we da turn a batch of fifty ewes on to it, August that'd be. Ivery one of 'em sound on all fours. Within a fortnight there by thirty a more, lame as trees. Aye, I reckon 'tis in the soil. They says a sheep's worst enemy is another sheep, an' that be right. Mind you, a wet time is worst, that's why I like me ewes ter run on pasture for a spell ter harden their feet. If a flock's ter do well their feet must be in proper fettle. No use a ewe spending her time praying – on 'er knees yer know – she needs be up an' feeding if she's agoin' ter feed 'ersel and 'er lambs.'

Edgar talked more to me now. Mind you, his comments were broken by long ruminative silences. This never seemed strange or tedious to me. Time was ours, all the time in the world it seemed. I hung on to his words as gold. They were never given lightly or easily and already I had had opportunity to glimpse the rough rock of experience from which they had been mined with such dogged courage and endurance.

26. 'The Looker'

Now that the ewes were all out on pasture in one field, which was an 'up and downer' containing several dellholes and dead ground, I had the daily job of walking round them, first thing in the morning and again in the evening. Edgar took a look during the day but this depended upon his legs. He hated missing his round but came to rely more and more upon my eyes.

I had also the tegs to look at but they were always less trouble in that being smaller and more active they ran less risk of getting 'cast'. I first heard this term when Edgar was giving me instructions on how to 'look'. 'Taint no use goin' round like they blokes on the Lunnon t' Brighton Walk tha knows. Ye'll see nuthin' an' might as well stay at 'ome. Walk right round and count 'em. If ye can't make the right number then look in the dellholes. I don't know as 'ow ye'll find any cast but. . .'

I broke in, 'What do you mean by "cast"?'

"Why bless me,' laughed the old man, 'on their backs and stranded like. They can die in a matter of owers, they do blow up an' suffocate. Ye mind that ole cart track runnin' along from Stoney Bottom ter Dickinson's land?'

'Yes, Edgar,' I replied.

'Well thas weer they'll be cast if anywheres. They do git in they ole cart tracks an' be cast.'

'But why do they get over?' I asked.

Edgar was getting impatient. 'Questyuns! Questyuns!' Then he stopped himself and smiled, 'Reckon I ought ter be plaised that ye care enuff ter wanter larn. Well I'll larn 'ee.'

He sat down on the worn steps and stretched his legs. 'We'm powerful near shearin'. Them ewes is carryin' a big fleece an' these showers we'm be 'avin' do wash the dust onto they backs. Come the sun an' they gets itchy, they wants ter roll an' scratch, they gits o'er and cos they've short legs an' broad ole backs they git cast.' He laughed. 'Na git goin' an' mind if yer gits one, doan' panic. Go to 'er slow, turn 'er on 'er side an' 'old 'er. Give 'er time ter get 'er breath an' then let 'er go. Sometimes when they'va bin over a long whiles, the heart won't stand the shock, an' if they rushes away in fright they be finished.'

As it happened that morning I had no untoward incidents, apart from one ewe that had stuck her head through one of the boundary nets and had to be released from her self-imposed stocks.

During the next week or two I enjoyed the job of 'lookin', it being a welcome change from the hurdled areas where we were folding the lambs on a bit of clover after-math. The ewes got to know me and would call, some drawing towards me, no doubt remembering the days when they were trough fed.

The hedges were gay with red campion and late clumps of pale primroses with their long hairy stems. Sometimes I strayed into Stoney Bottom, startling the bullfinches which flitted furtively amongst the massed briar roses and causing the great green woodpecker to rise from an ant hill in a glory of scarlet crown, green and gold-dusted plumage.

27. *The Pastryboard*

The lambs were growing apace and already we had some really good ram lambs. We had split them now into two folds, ewe lambs in one and ram lambs with wethers in the other.

I always loved the field we were in, it went by the name of Beech Spinney and lay on both sides of the little valley above Stoney Bottom. A belt of trees, mostly ash and oak with an occasional lordly beech, ran along the field's north-eastern boundary and gave welcome shelter from the wind. The trees reached out like a long arm right up to the

Spinney. It was a field which seemed to trap the sun, and the deer from Ashridge Common often came there, especially when turnips were growing in it.

I had just given the lambs their corn and nuts and opened the hurdles for the lambs to run on, when I saw a lamb lying in the fold. As I approached the lamb I realised that it was dead. It was a big ram lying on its side, the legs stuck out straight from the body, as stiff as stilts. Edgar saw me carrying it up to the fold, from the door of the caravan. 'Lay it down there Davey. Fetch me a bucket of water and I'll get the pastry board.' By the time I got back from the water-cart Edgar was bending over the lamb. He stood the dead lamb on its legs and said 'Watch.' He released his hold and the lamb fell over like a child's woolly toy. 'Notice anything Davey?'

'Well,' I said, 'it's stiff as a board and there's a lot of froth about the mouth.'

He nodded 'That's pulpy kidney lad. Now you know what ter do. Open it up. I'll put the kettle on.'

The pastryboard scrubbed white stood against the wheel of the caravan. I found a level place on the steps and laid it flat, placing the bucket of water next to it. Then with my knife I opened the lamb and placed all the organs upon the board. Edgar peered over the botton half of the door 'Good lad, yer getting farster. Roight, go through 'em.'

I picked up the lungs, 'Lungs – not a bad colour,' I said.

'Drop 'em in the bucket,' ordered Edgar. I did and they dropped below the surface, to rise again and float. 'They be arright, if they sinks ye mun look for pewmonia,' he grunted approvingly.

'Heart – normal size, not fatty but firm.' I looked up at him as I made the comment.

'Aye – go on.'

'Liver – sound – no sign of disease or fluke. Kidneys. . .' I stopped. I had a job to pick them up. I had noticed when I laid them on the board that they seemed somehow slippery and discoloured.

'Take 'old o' one and press it between yer fingers,' said Edgar. I did so and my fingers met in the middle. 'See that – that be pulpy kidney. It's always the best lambs go this way. Yer see they tends ter eat ower much. The young green ferments in the stomach and a poison starts — toxic they calls it an' they reckon that goes fer the kidneys. Happens so sudden some call it "strike".'

'Can't you do anything Edgar?' I asked.

'Aye, an' we doos, ivery lamb gits an injection when they be born, for dysentery an' pulpy kidney, but I reckon they needs a booster afore they comes on ter a lot o' grub.'

'Let's look at the stomach Davey, then 'ave yer tea an' ye can bury un arter.'

The stomach was clear, only traces of inflammation, probably from the toxin. I swilled the board down and put it to dry in the sun. Looking down the fold of the lambs, I wondered how many more would fall victims.

Edgar was always the same, if a ewe or lamb died, he tried to find out why. Sometimes he could prevent further deaths. As in this case he was careful to keep the lambs back until the dew was off the green. We gave a bit of sweet hay — not that they ate much, but it helped to fill them before going on. The trough food also helped in this way. Sometimes Edgar would leave them on the new fold for a spell and then pull them back to clear up behind on the old fold, before putting them on again.

Later the booster shot became common practice and pulpy kidney increasingly rare though season and available feed had a lot to do with the occurrence of it.

We never had a Vet out to the flock, lambing time or any other time. Edgar was master of his craft and I don't know that anyone ever suggested to him that we should call in outside help.

It may seem odd that we kept the wethers with the ram lambs, but this was only until we were sure that the castration had been effective. This was soon discernible in most cases and the scrotum shrivelled. One of the criticisms of the bloodless method is that the cords may not be completely severed and, of course, this means that the lamb is still potent as a ram. I cannot remember this happening whilst I was with Edgar. Others say that the wethers produced by this method develop characteristics which are too masculine, and that this has adverse effects upon the meat, it being stronger. We only seemed to hit trouble when dealing with 'rigs'. This term applies to ram lambs that retain a testicle in the abdomen, so that only one descends into the scrotum. This presents a problem as we can only deal with the descended testicle and although the ram is impotent, the sperm being sterile by virtue of having been produced at body temperature, these 'rigs' still retain all the male characteristics and are always a nuisance. We got rid of them to the butcher as soon as possible, not that we ever had more than one or two to cope with.

28. *The Duel*

The shepherd likes to think of himself as king of the farm, at least when the cowman is not in earshot, for they are always fighting over the pasture and feed available. In this case it was a friendly rivalry but there were times when feelings rose pretty high: in Winter time when Edgar did his best to collar the sweetest hay for his lambing flock and again in the early part of the year when all eyes were looking with longing for the first bit of grass. The cowman was also eagerly awaiting the day when he could turn the cows out and be finished with the endless routine of mucking out cowsheds, racking up and bedding down stock at night. He needed the grass, too, so that the milk yield would pick up, apart from the bonus it would bring him, if he was paid according to milk yield.

Edgar was just as anxious that his ewes should have a bite of sweet grass — there was nothing like it to help his milking ewes and if the kale situation was bad, his need was desperate. We could plan ahead in the way of kale and roots, setting out marrow-stem kale for the back end of the year, with thousand head kale which could stand intense frost and cold, to follow on in the Winter and early Spring. Yet all our planning could be set at nought if brown heart struck the swedes and they went rotten — or a spell of snow, 'white over' as we called it, brought the grey pigeon hordes from across the sea to sit like giant blue-grey aphids on the kale tops. There were so many at times that the kale became invisible, a shot sent them up like a clap of thunder which darkened the sky with a swirl of wings, but they would be back again after another meal on the clover ley. We hated them and feared them, a grey sea which washed over what green we had, which on its ebbing left but yellowed stumps and the stink of rottenness.

The bailiff usually acted as umpire for naturally he wanted both sides of the farm to do well. He would talk with Edgar and offer him a rick of hay and the old shepherd knowing very well where the best hay had been taken, would plump immediately for the best rick. In this we usually got our way as the sheep were more fastidious feeders than the cows and young stock. Pasture rights could be fixed fairly easily as we obviously had to have grass handy to the the lambing yard, the sheep moving each year around the farm and keeping to the sunny sheltered spots. Moving was important in order to avoid disease, giving old sites some seasons in which to sweeten up.

The dual never ceased, but Edgar and Jess had a deep built-in respect for each other, they were, after all, stockmen and masters of their craft.

Edgar was nothing if not forthright. I remember one morning during my second lambing season, Mr. A.P. Good, the owner of the estate, arrived at the lambing yard with two dogs for company. His smiling face beamed at Edgar. 'Good morning, Kirby,' he called.

Edgar looked up from the ewe he was attending. 'It were ye means. Tak them bloody dawgs away from my sheep an' if yer come agin, leave 'em at 'ome.'

I busied myself with unusual enthusiasm in the job of scraping some corn boxes clean and held my breath.

A.P.G. as we called him amongst ourselves, was immediate contrition. 'Eh, I am sorry Kirby. I ought to have known better. I'll take them back now' and off he went.

I told Harry about the old man's belligerence. 'Anyone would have thought that they were Edgar's sheep, Harry, the way he spoke.'

'They are his sheep,' came the reply.

'But they. . .' I began to protest.

'No buts about it, lad,' laughed Harry. 'That's why Edgar is a shepherd. He looks after that flock just as if they were his own. God help anyone, Mr. Good, included, that puts one of his sheep in jeopardy. Mr. Good understands that, he's not stupid.'

Harry went on, 'Did you know that Edgar was once a shepherd at Sandringham? The story is told of how Queen Mary came to the lambing yard in a post car with her lady-in-waiting. After being shown round the Queen turned to get into her car and old Edgar rapped out 'Ye'll not be getting in there wi' that muck on yer shoe!' They say the lady-in-waiting looked horrified, but the old Queen, she turned and smiling, wiped her shoe on the grass. Old Edgar's a law unto himself, I suppose, but the old varmint is solid gold.'

29. *Farm Workers*

As the seasons passed, I became more and more aware of the complex farm jigsaw of which the sheep and shepherd were just a part. A jigsaw in fact without which the flock could not exist. Edgar, Harry and myself worked with the sheep in our little piece and at times it became almost possible to feel that we were quite independent, a self-supporting unit. Those were the days when we folded the wide acres and saw no-one for days on end, a calm, measured, peaceful life which I savoured and loved. I say almost, because as the burden and urgency of seasonal work thrust itself upon the life of the farm, the bailiff would appear in the field. I would see him out of the corner of my eye as he reined in his mare and had a 'bit talk' with Edgar. Then off he would go, cantering up the field with faithful Nell tailing behind. A shout from Edgar would follow, 'Davey!' and resignedly I would walk over to him. 'Bailiff wants yer hoeing in Barn Ground, the mangles need singlin'. Bloomin' nuisance but there tis. 'ee sez ter git 'ome fer dinner an' bring zum tay — ye'll be workin' over a bit.

Coom ter me in t'mornin' like ye allus does.'

Hoeing I enjoyed mainly because all the men possible were gathered. We often hoed twenty or more strong. There was a deep sense of community. We youngsters would tear away up our row like hares at first, but we soon tired and dropped back to a much slower pace than the old hands. Then they showed their true worth, having finished their row, they would turn back down ours and work on till we met, then we would all shoulder hoes and go back for a 'spit and draw' as they said, before tackling another drift.

The man responsible for stacking hay, building ricks and thatching, always seemed to have a mystique about him. He was often the hedger on the farm as well, with an eye on potential hazel pegs that he would eventually need for thatching.

On our farms we were expected to load our own waggon and unload it at the rick, before being allowed on the rick itself. There was good sense in this. It was no easy matter coping with the fusillade of sheaves that came winging towards you. Two men would be pitching from the stooks on either side of the waggon, which would stop between four stooks. The waggon would have barely stopped, when the bombardment would start. Sheaves flying everywhere, twenty-four in as many seconds. Then 'Hold tight' and the waggon would lurch forward. You soon learnt to shout 'on the front' or 'I'll take 'em in the middle' or 'back ladder.' The secret lay in keeping the middle of the load full, then doing a couple of layers round the outside, then filling up the middle again. In this way, the outer sheaves were bound in by the weight of the middle and prevented from slipping. I used my hands and got so used to the movement of the waggon, that even as we lurched up between the rows, I could go on laying the sheaves in the middle. Otherwise, when we reached the rick with a towering load, it was hard work unloading. The tidier the load, the easier it was to unload.

One day I rode up to the rick, lying on my back and enjoying the swaying ride and watching the white bee-skep clouds sailing across the blue sky. We stopped and I stood up, waiting to unload. One of the men handed me up my fork — tines first, which was the rule. The rick builder, Harry Durrant, hailed me. 'I want you along side o' me, David. Time you came on the rick.'

The elevator clacked into life and we started. I was second man, feeding Harry. Sheaves had to be presented butt first, not in his face but just near enough for him to grab. He worked round and round the rick, building with his hands. Durrant worked backwards, kneeling all the time. He wore leather knee pads, strapped on. I kept him supplied and filled up to the middle as we went. The outer sheaves had to have a slight downward tilt to run the rain off the rick and not into its heart. Time and again the old man would yell 'Whoa.' He would creak to his feet and descend the ladder and take a slow walk round the growing rick, giving it a long hard look. Sometimes he'd take an implement like a notice board and give part of the rick an almighty thwack! Then back again up the ladder. Rather rashly I made bold to ask him, after this had happened several times, 'Mr. Durrant, why do you get down so often?'

For a moment I thought he was going to explode. Then the impending storm veered away and with a smile he said, 'Well, I reckon you're only larning. If ye wanna see yer work, yer must get off and stand back. When a' does that a' sees my father's ricks. He was a master. Then a' looks at this un a' mine an' a' knows whether I be going out too far, or pulling in too much. Let's get on, 'twill soon be night else.'

30. *Shearing*

It must have been early June when Edgar told me to walk over to Cold Harbour Farm to help with the shearing. 'Jest carry they 'urdles forrward fer I an' then ye can be off ter Harry.'

'Did you like shearing Edgar?' I asked as I dropped a load of hurdles off my shoulder onto the clover.

'Dunno as I minded but me ole legs is parst that caper na. Ower much kneelin' and a'bending like.' He looked at

me and laughed, 'Tis nowt ter fuss abaht. Ye'll like un. An'
anyways Harry'll put ye roight.'

Soon I was on my way to Cold Harbour. I must admit
that my progress was schoolboy-like. A new job always
worked me up and though I had got very used to Edgar's
rough tongue, so that working with Harry was much less
demanding, I still felt more confident with the old man.
To some folk it might have been annoying but Edgar never
assumed that I knew how to do a new job, he would explain
his method first, then give me a practical demonstration
before letting me loose as it were. Once I had mastered the
job in hand he left me alone to get on. He might and often
did make a caustic comment if I wasn't up to standard —
Edgar's standard — but I quickly learnt that there was
always a very good reason for doing things in a certain way.

I walked along the cart-track until I reached the edge of
the bean field, still fragrant with black and white flowers,
then I turned down the headland to Furzen Wood. I didn't
have to go that way, but the old wood fascinated me. The
bluebells were over, already their green seed pods were
well formed. I entered the main ride which would lead me
out directly in line with Cold Harbour. It was a dark wood
— small in area but big with mystery. Beneath the great
trees, chestnut, cherry, ash and oak, grew high tangled
thorns, festooned with heavy green curtains of old man's
beard — the wild clematis. Here grew the loveliest sprays of
honeysuckle — white trumpet clusters in the wood's half-
light. I stopped a moment by the gamekeeper's gibbet —
Johnstone had been busy. I hated seeing the grey javelin
sparrowhawk which hung dishevelled and still, side by side
with magpie, jay, carrion crow, and the long lean racing
bodies of black-tipped stoat and smaller weasel, their
needle teeth snarling wickedly in death.

A speckled wood butterfly danced in the sunlight and
shadow of the ride, to disappear as it settled, wings up-
lifted, upon a bramble leaf.

The wood ended and Cold Harbour lay before me, two
short fields away.

'You've come then young un,' said Harry as he wiped
the sweat from his forehead with a bare forearm. He was

half bent over a ewe which sat quietly against his legs.

'I came straight from the fold Harry, when I'd finished helping Edgar. Sorry if I'm late,' I added trying to look contrite.

'Oh, and since when has Furzen Wood been the quickest way here,' he retorted. I must have looked properly caught out, for Harry burst out laughing. 'Not to worry and don't go thinkin' I'm psychic. I went to the yard gate for a smoke and saw the pigeons flying out of the wood. I guessed it was you.'

Harry took up the shearing head. 'I'll just finish this ewe off and then I'll tell you what to do.' He turned round and switched the power on, the head leapt in to clacking life and Harry's shearing hand began to move swiftly round the ewe. Seconds later he switched off, hung the head up and still holding the ewe, guided her out of the shearing pen and let her run into the fold yard.

'First job, Davey, is to learn how to roll a fleece. Watch.' Harry lifted the fleece up, it hung in one piece. With a flick of his wrists he threw out the fleece so that it landed shorn side down upon the canvas covering of the shearing pen. 'Before we roll it we take off any soiled wool — like this.' Harry bent down and pulled away several pieces from the tail and he continued 'We call these tailings.' He took the handful of wool and pushed it down into the sack, which hung in a corner of the pen. 'This goes in with the dagging wool — it all fetches something.' He bent down closer to the fleece 'Come here, Davey, see that!' He pointed to where he had pulled the pieces off. I looked closely at the wool, nothing registered except the obvious fact that this was wool! 'See those white fibres. That's what we call kemp. It's rough, brittle and useless — like dog hairs. If you're going to find it in a fleece it will be in the britching wool — the sides of the hind legs. Though sometimes you can see it on the crown of the head.'

'Right now, I'll roll the fleece for you.' Harry turned the sides into the middle, forming a long narrow rectangle. Then he turned the tail end in and began to roll the fleece, making a tight roll. He placed a foot on it to hold it in place and took hold of the neck wool. This he wound round and round his wrist alternately pulling the wool out and twisting it until he had made a wool rope. 'You mustn't pull it too hard at first,' said Harry. 'Else it'll come away from the fleece. Now as I hold the roll tight I wind the wool rope round and tuck the end in.' He took the tightly rolled fleece and threw it onto the pile of fleeces stacked in the adjoining pen of hurdles. It bounced and settled on the pile without shifting. 'Think you can do it?'

I nodded. 'I'll do my best, Harry.'

'That's the boy,' said the shepherd. 'One job at a time. As I shear 'em dab a bit of paint on the shoulder — the red paint by the gate — and let 'em out. Then roll the wool, whilst I catch another. Remember roll 'em tight.'

'Wouldn't twine be quicker for tying?' I queried.

'No fear, Davey,' laughed Harry. 'Twin would get entangled in the wool and cause a lot of trouble. Knocks down the price too. Now let's get cracking.'

For the next three days I helped Harry, eager now to finish the jobs in the fold and walk over to Cold Harbour. It was on one of these mornings that I saw four squirrels meet a violent death. The cart-track which crossed Stoney Bottom on the way to Cold Harbour had been raised high by repeated tipping of stones and rubble in order to combat the water that gathered in the bed of the valley. Now it thrust across the middle like a long mole. Strangely enough, water still gathered there even in high Summer. Edgar reckoned a spring rose below the road. Tall poles carried electricity across the valley at this point, taking advantage of the gap in the trees, and at the corner where they swung left to follow the winding trail towards Cold Harbour farm stood a double master pole to carry the weight of the wires as they abruptly changed direction. The long finger of wood which ran from Beech Spinney finished at this point and gave place to thorn bushes and tangled clematis. As I neared the master pole I heard a commotion in the trees ahead and saw a group of grey squirrels tearing like mad things through the tree-tops. The lead squirrel was chattering away as it flung itself from branch to branch; suddenly there were no more trees and with one leap it was on the pole. There was a sharp crack and it dropped stone dead to the field below. In the time I have written this there were three more cracks and a smell of burning and four squirrels lay rigid in death at the foot of the pole. I looked at them as I passed, the fore-paws and the tail of each one were singed brown, and the fleas were already running about their bodies in agitation.

Somewhere along the wood a jay cursed and as the light winds stirred the bean flowers a turtle dove came and sat in the cherry tree to croon of Summer.

Once with Harry there was little respite; he never seemed to tire. Each night he kept a score of ewes in the covered yard, which had been cleaned out. It was dry and unstained and gave him a good start in the morning. Rain the night before or a heavy dew meant that we would have had to wait for the ewes to dry out, if they had been lying in the open.

'No good shearing damp sheep,' said Harry. 'It dries better on them, than hanging shorn fleeces over hurdles.'

I had now got into the routine and would regularly sweep the canvas so that Harry could get on more quickly. Droppings and soiled bits of wool — straw wisps and the like — had no place on the shearing floor. On the fourth day Harry greeted me as usual and then said 'We'll have you shearing today, Davey.' I looked rather anxiously at the machine. Harry laughed, 'No lad, we'll start you on the hand shears. You can't do so much damage with them. I'll clip one and show you the way, then you can try the next.'

He looked at the waiting ewes and then pointed 'See that ewe with the wool coming away from her neck? Catch her!' I brought her struggling into the pen. Harry caught her round the neck and turned her. She sat quietly and easily against his knees. He reached up, took a pair of shears off the bales behind and removed them from their leather scabbard. 'I asked you to pick this ewe,' said Harry, 'because the wool had risen.' He pulled back the wool that was coming away at the ewe's neck. 'Look closer.'

I bent down. He continued 'The wool nearest the skin is new wool, the beginning of a new fleece in fact. Now just above it — can you see a brownish line?'

'Yes, Harry,' I answered.

'Well that's the oil from off the skin — that's what we call risen. When you shear, you go under that line — more or less — and the fleece lifts off.'

Harry straightened up and pointed again towards the waiting sheep. 'See that poor ewe in the corner — she's got a tight fleece. If I sheared her now, I'd be ploughing through thick grease. Her fleece hasn't risen — perhaps it never will properly — I'll have to rive it off. There's an old saying "A wealthy sheep gives her fleece easily" — a good text for a parson. Poor ewes hang on to theirs,' he laughed. 'Righto we'll make a start. First I open the neck.' He clipped down the neck and breast of the sheep, clearing away the wool from the breast bone, talking away to me as he went. 'It's easier for me to teach you Davey for we're both left-handed — though I can use both at this game.' Next came the head. I noticed how he bent the head away from himself, shearing the neck and side of the face nearest him, then bending it over towards himself to clear the wool on the other side, holding each ear down in turn so as not to cut them.

Then he held the fore-leg — the right fore-leg — the other being against himself, and sheared it clean. Holding it up he clipped under and round it taking long clacking sweeps to the centre of the back. When he had got as low as he could, bending from the waist, Harry let the ewe slip down between his legs and he knelt astride her shearing the back leg and tail.

Next Harry, with the ewe still lying flat, swung round, so that his left leg pinned the ewe's head down, her right fore-legs he tucked behind his knee then with his right arm between her hind legs and holding the right hind leg back out of the way he began to shear away the belly wool going very carefully around the teats.

This done he lifted the ewe up again and facing her the other way repeated the process on the other side — his swathes of wool meeting along the spine and allowing the fleece to fall around the ewe like a lovely white gown. The second stage was quicker as the fiddly bits — head and belly — were already clean, and very soon he allowed the ewe to drop to her feet looking shorn, white and rather bewildered.

'We've got about half an hour to dinnertime Davey. I'll let you shear the next and watch you through it,' said Harry. 'Pick your ewe.'

I marked with my eye the ewe I wanted and moved into the pen. I had long since learnt that to catch a sheep quickly, one had to decide on one and then look anywhere but directly at her. In this way it was possible to move in close, before she realised that she was the one selected, and grab her. I caught her first time and drew her onto the sheet. The next moment she was sitting easily against my legs. I reached back for my shears — removing the scabbard as I had seen Harry do before me. 'Just a word before you start,' Harry called, as he stuffed the last bits of tail wool from the previous ewe into the sack. 'Two things to remember always. Never, and I mean never, put your shears down without the scabbard on when you're shearing. If you can't reach the scabbard put the shears right out of your way — on the bales like. I've seen a sheep killed by rolling onto open shears. Secondly, if you hold your sheep right, the wool will always fall away from your shears and leave your cutting line clean. Got it? Don't let me see you having to push the wool away and it keep falling back over your cut. Now off you go — small snips and just the flat of the blades on the body of the ewe. There's nothing to stop you using your free hand to pull the shorn skin towards you to keep it tight.'

Gingerly at first, but slowly gaining confidence, I sheared my sheep. Harry took me through the tricky bits. Once or twice I nicked the ewe and she jumped in protest. 'Now you see why I wanted you to learn with hand shears,' said Harry. 'When you are not holding her right the skin loses its tension and wrinkles — with that machine clipper you could take a whole slice of skin off easy as winking. Might not look much, but wait till she stands up!'

I had almost finished one side and began to clear the belly wool. 'Hold on,' said Harry. 'She'll beat you if you're not sitting right. That's it now, left leg over the neck and tuck her right fore-leg behind your knees — as you sit back you'll pin it. Now, right hand in.' I moved my right arm between her legs, blocking the right hind leg.

'Good lad — you've got it.'

We were a little late in finishing for dinner, but I had sheared my first sheep. I appreciated what Edgar had said about bending. I felt that I had used every muscle on my body as I straightened up with an 'Ouch.'

Harry grinned. 'By the time we've finished the flock — tups and all — you'll be really fit.'

I looked at my overalls shining with grease and wondered what on earth my landlady would say. Harry saw my concern. 'After dinner I'll fit you up with an old pair for shearing and you can slip 'em off before you go home.'

During the following days I learnt more about the shape of a sheep's body than I had ever dreamt possible, and Harry loved talking about wool.

31. *The Golden Fleece*

'Come and have a look at this fleece Davey,' called Harry. By this time, almost at the end of shearing, we were shearing side by side. Shearing our own sheep and rolling our own fleeces. 'Billy just left school' was catching and paint-marking the ewes for us and sweeping up. We were now running two heads off the machine and I found the work much quicker and easier on the hand and wrist muscles.

The fleece in question lay flung out on the sheet. 'Long time since I saw that in this flock.' He pointed to the tail end of the fleece — there was a patch of dark brown wool. 'There's the ewe, the one Billy's got hold of. See the spot?' Billy was just marking her and I saw immediately the half crown of brown on her left flank. 'She'll be drafted this time,' said Harry. 'No sense in breeding from her again. Hold her Billy!' he yelled as the boy made to release her.

We went over and Harry parted what wool there was on the neck. 'What colour is the skin Davey?'

'Pink', I replied.

Harry moved to the brown blot on his shepherd's horizon. 'What colour is the skin under that?'

'Why, it is black,' I said in surprise.

'Aye, the wrong pigment. I thought I'd got rid of the last in the flock. Must have been three summers gone, we bought in a good ram, but he threw a lot of lambs with black spots and that's no good to a pedigree flock of Southdowns. Come here and I'll show you.' We walked back over to the fleece. 'Feel that dark wool — what do you make of it?' I ran my fingers through the brown fibres.

'It's coarser — rather like the kemp — the dog hair wool you showed me before.'

'See the difference in this,' said Harry as he pulled a sample of wool from the middle of the same fleece. 'It's got everything wool should have — see how the fibres cling together.' He drew out about a dozen or so fibres and held them up against the sunlight, which streamed into the shed. They shone like gold. 'We call that lustre. Good wool should be long and strong.' He pulled the wool between his two hands. 'See it give — what the text-book calls elasticity!' He grinned. 'Look how the fine fibres are — a bit different from that old kempy brown tack, and notice that the fibres are somewhat about the same length, sort of uniform.' He dropped the wool and started to turn in and roll the fleece. 'Pity about that spot,' he muttered. 'It's a fine piece of wool. I'll make sure that won't go in. Might spoil the sample.' He rose to his feet. 'Tell you what Davey. I'll have a word with the bailiff, if you're interested, and we'll look at some wool through his microscope.'

I gasped, 'Oh yes, please.'

'That's on then,' laughed Harry. 'We'll make a flock master of you yet. Did you know when you look at a fibre of wool through the microscope you can actually see when the ewe has been through a hard time — the fibre's weakest at that point and that is where it will break under tension.'

As I walked home from Cold Harbour, I thought much about shepherds and shepherding, there seemed to be no end to the skills and knowledge one needed.

32. *The Hireling*

It was good when the shearing was finished to see the ewes run onto the pasture to fan out and graze or sit and ruminate, scattered about the hillside like white stones upon the green grass. As soon as they had grown enough wool we prepared to dip them. As Edgar said, 'They'da need enuf wool ter hold the dip.' Dipping is, of course, compulsory to ward off the possibilities of sheep scab, not only this, the dip got rid of any unwelcome lodgers — sheep ticks or keds. We were not troubled with the latter, partly due to the fact that our flock was folded and the fleece was so dense. In hill sheep running the fells and moors, ticks could be a real menace, not only weakening the sheep with their blood-sucking habits, but by being the carriers of disease. Dipping also discouraged the attentions of the blowflies and gave a welcome respite to the ewes.

The Summer that year was a real scorcher and the sheep sought the shade beneath the great elm trees. Harry decided to dip on Tuesday and the local policeman was informed of our intention. According to the book he was supposed to stand by and check the time each ewe spent in the dip and also to ensure that each and every one was totally immersed. In practice this was virtually impossible, but he would come when possible and officiate, joining in the general chaff and high spirits that accompanied 'dipping'. Sometimes he would take off his jacket and lend a hand. Ted was working with us then, Edgar being off to Droitwich for salt bath treatment for his legs, agreeing to go after much persuasion by the boss, who thought the world of the old man and wanted to help him. 'Be like a real holiday Edgar,' said Harry, 'and all expenses paid.' Edgar had gone off to the Spa, outwardly still protesting but inwardly pleased that the boss valued him so highly.

Ted now helped me with the folding and I felt quite a bit taller, being left in charge of the lambs. Ted had never worked much with sheep before, indeed it was difficult to find out what he had been, before coming to the farm. There was a wildness about him, and he always reminded me of a pot just on the simmer, as if it would take very little to make him erupt into violence. He was tall and well-made with a thatch of hair like straw, fresh complexioned and very light blue eyes. His hands were immense and raw boned, it seemed as though everything he did was done with the maximum of effort. I tried to show Ted that it was only necessary to tap the heads of the hurdles, to let the toe into the ground, but it was no use. Ted wielded the bar like an executioner's axe. I had begun to wonder how many hurdles would be left intact by the time Edgar returned. The position was made more difficult by the fact that I must have been ten years Ted's junior. Harry came when he could to the fold, but he was busy preparing sheep for showing and his visits were comparatively rare.

There was another thing which cut right across my idea of what a stockman, let alone a shepherd, should be like — the time factor. Come five o'clock and Ted downed tools and was away, as far as knocking off was concerned he was up to the minute, starting work was different! 'Ten-to-five Davey,' Ted would shout across the fold. 'Time I'm out of the field, it'll be five.' The idea of finishing his line of hurdles before going never occurred to him, nor the need to walk round the lambs before shutting up the caravan. I shuddered to think what would happen at lambing time; yet when I thought about Edgar, I guessed that a partnership between Ted and himself would probably be very short-lived indeed. The end came sooner than I had dreamt before Edgar returned and in a way that is burned upon my mind.

I have said that Harry proposed dipping on Tuesday morning. The flock was lying over in a field near Cold Harbour, Oak Meadow I think. Monday was very hot and by the 'glass', Tuesday would be like it. Harry came down to the lamb fold in the late afternoon and had a word with me. 'I'd like Ted to go over to Cold Harbour and bring the ewes over to Home Farm Meadow, against the dipping pen. If we leave 'em till morning the sun will be well up before we can start moving 'em and they'll get here all hot and panting and that's no good for dipping.'

'Let me go, Harry,' I said.

'No lad,' he replied. 'You finish off here and then come up to the dipping pens. I need you to help me mix the dip and get things ready for morning.' He turned, 'Ted — here a minute.'

I went on pitching and a few minutes later when I glanced up Ted had gone and Harry was striding away towards the farm.

I finished my fold and after checking the lambs and rescuing one that had its head stuck in the netting, I walked across to Harry. It must have been twenty-to-five when we had finished preparing the dip. We placed the cover back over it as a safety precaution and sorted out the 'possers' or 'pushers', leaving these against the rails alongside the dip. Possers were like small yokes on long shafts, to push the ewes under the surface of the dip as they swam along; they were also useful in pushing ewes out, if they were slow in hurrying up the ramp, where they would stand in the draining pens, before being released into the meadow again. Harry and I stood leaning against the pens, enjoying a smoke and grateful for the shade of the maple trees which overhung the pens at one corner. Harry looked at his watch, which he kept in an old tin, padded with cotton wool. ''Bout ten minutes ter five,' he murmured. 'Ted won't be long. I let him take Owd Bob and George said that he'd help turn 'em onto the trace from Cold Harbour.

George the pigman was in charge of some thirty breeding sows, mostly pedigree Wessex. I knew him to be as fine a pigman as Harry and Edgar were shepherds, and they bore each other a mutual respect.

The minutes ticked by and we gazed out over the great meadow, a silken carpet of ryegrass, red sorrel and buttercup gold which shimmered in the heat, so that it hurt the eyes to look for too long. Even the great hedgerow elms and oaks seemed to move as fluid to the eyes, one moment clear, the next dissolving into green blurs of heat haze.

Harry started from his easy position against the rails. 'What the hell. . .' Across the meadow came a cloud of dust, we could hear a confused baaing and Ted's voice yelling 'Ho! Ho there!'

'It's the bloody ewes,' swore Harry, 'an' that silly bugger's driving 'em.'

The flock rolled nearer, we could see the ewes racing forward. Ted was circling to and fro behind them on his bicycle! He reached us, leapt from his bike and whipped out his watch all in one movement. 'Minute ter five. Just made it. Time's time, yer know. There's a couple couldn't keep up, I left 'em behind on the track. Well I'll be. . .'

Harry had jumped forward and caught hold of Ted's bike by the handlebars. He was shaking with rage. I hardly dared look at him. It took Harry all his time to get the words out. 'A minute ter five is it, yer rotten time serving bastard. Get on that bike and never come near my ewes again. Yer not a shepherd — never will be — yer a hireling!'

Ted was gone, ewes were lying down and panting like dogs. We left them and walked back along the track. The two ewes were dead when we reached them, blood oozing from their nostrils. Harry walked back with me to the farm, swearing terribly, blaming himself for not seeing until too late, what Ted was like. 'Now yer know Davey, why old Edgar has no time for clock watchers in the fold. That's the difference, sheep come first with him, they're his sheep and his life. There aren't many left of his stamp — an' more's the pity.'

33. *Dipping*

On Tuesday morning we assembled at the dipping pen. Billy and I were to do the catching. Harry ran the ewes into the two large gathering pens and two of the cowmen came out to wield the possers and assist the sheep through the dip. We all wore oilskins or old rain coats, the old hands knew without any telling, but Harry warned Billy and myself that we would soon get drenched if we did not. Billy and I filled the smaller pen nearest the entry to the dip with ewes. Harry dropped the ewes in at the deep end where the concrete wall was vertical. He turned each ewe so that she was sitting up and eased her hindquarters over the edge and dropped her down. The ewes went right

under, then bobbed up spluttering and swam to the far end
of the bath. The concrete sloped gradually up until it
reached a long ramp, ribbed with shallow steps, and the
ewes walked out. If a ewe failed to go under, she was
hooked under the head by a posser and made to swim
again to the deep end and ducked once more. Often there
were three sheep in the dip and the hubbub and laughter
mingled with the cries of the ewes. Occasionally a ewe
would career past Billy and myself and take a flying leap
into the dip, landing with a tremendous splash and shower-
ing everyone, but nine times out of ten, the ewes would
hang back and showed the greatest reluctance to take the
plunge. After dipping the ewes stood for a while in the
draining pens and the dipping fluid ran down the herring-
bone pattern of channels in the sloping concrete and back
into the dip.

By dinnertime the ewes were all through and grazing
contentedly over the pasture. We left them in peace and
when Harry and I got back we took Owd Bob and walked
them gently back over to the 'up and downer' field beyond
Dan East wood.

The lambs were still to be dipped, but we were leaving
that until the next day. It would be a much easier job and
that was a comforting thought! On my return from taking
the ewes I walked back through Christmas Tree Valley to
the lamb fold. It was cool amongst the dark green spruce
and feathered larches. A goldcrest in the conifers sang in
that slight whispering voice that seems so much a part of
the wind's song, and up on the cleared shoulder of the
valley a grasshopper warbler was 'spinning his reel'. I had
half a mind to look for the bee orchids there, but the
lambs were on my mind and I quickened my stride
towards them.

All was well in the fold. I felt satisfied. I was two folds
ahead and felt that if Edgar had come into the field he
would have been pleased, but no such luck, the old man
had a habit of appearing on the scene when I was in a right
muddle!

A quick, but not too quick, look round the lambs and I
was away back to the dip, to give the pens — now filthy

from the passage of the ewes — a good sweep and swill out before the lambs went through.

34. *Show Time*

In my first year I went to no shows, at least as far as our flock was concerned. Edgar and Harry would discuss the merits of various rams which were shown singly and the pens of three ewes. They would perhaps enter three shearling rams and two pens of shearling ewes. These were last year's lambs and would be got ready for show this June. Most of the shows were held in late May, June and early July, and Harry would take a string or group round the big shows. Names like the Three Counties, Bath and West, and The Royal fell with easy familiarity from his lips. Edgar no longer went 'trottin' round' the shows as he put it, his old legs were past it and the rough lying did him no good. Later on I had good reason to appreciate what he meant.

Despite the fact that I was as yet too green to be sent with Harry, I spent many evenings and odd hours watching him prepare his sheep for the judges.

The rams and ewes selected for showing and indeed all the rams for sale were not sheared completely but half shorn. In a year's crop of lambs we might have a dozen really tip-top rams to be sold for pedigree breeding in Southdown flocks, of those perhaps only three or four would be selected for showing. The best of the ram lambs would be sold as shearling rams at the Flock Society sale at Chichester and the rest would be bought for crossing with other breeds, the resultant half-bred lambs would not only possess the hybrid vigour of a first cross, but also the quality of early maturing from the Southdown and make first class lambs for grading. Harry said that the growing popularity of the larger Suffolk — also one of the Down breeds — was tending to hit the sale of Southdown field rams for crossing.

The only ewes to be half shorn were the pens of three for showing. If they did well at shows, they would naturally attract buyers keen to find good type ewes, as replacements for their own breeding flock. As a rule we drafted in about forty homebred shearling ewes into our flock each year to replace losses through death, barrenness, and age. We called the latter 'draft ewes' and they normally went to the butcher for sale as they became fat. Ewe lambs not wanted for breeding or sale were sold off with the wethers as soon as they were fit for the butcher.

Ewes normally stayed in the breeding flock for six to eight years. Everything depended upon the state of their teeth, as a ewe lost her teeth through age, she became less efficient as a feeder — both in providing for herself and, of course, for her lambs, whether unborn or sucking. These ewes were termed 'broken mouthed' and away they went as soon as they had put on enough flesh to make it worthwhile; they were sold for meat.

Mountain sheep are different in that when they are drafted from their flocks as broken mouthed they are sought after by lowland farmers, who will buy them in very cheaply as draft ewes, get one crop of lambs and then sell both ewes and lambs in late Spring for slaughter, buying in a new batch the following late Summer. These are known as 'flying flocks'.

The mountain ewes thrive despite being broken mouthed because conditions are by comparison so much easier. Not only this but they are easy lambers, being older ewes, and give very little trouble. A Down ram would normally be used on these ewes.

However, I must go back to the half shearing. Harry had told me that he would be starting to prepare the rams for show and I hurried up to the sheep shed after tea to watch him at work. He had already got a ram fixed in the stock, its head held firmly in the V of wood by an iron bolt which slipped through a hole in each arm. The ram stood quietly on the canvas sheet, the more so because Harry had covered its head with a piece of sacking. He had already trimmed the back wool, leaving it as flat as a board. 'Well Davey, come to learn a few more tricks have you?' I nodded. 'See that,' said Harry pointing to the level back. 'Put your hand along it and feel the back bone.' I put my hand on the sheep, not knowing quite what to look for.

'No, not like that.' Harry laughed and came round to where I was standing. 'Stand to one side of your sheep, and place your hand first round the dock — tail end you know. Feel the width of it then move your hand forward along the back, press down with your flat hand, fingers pointing to the front, then lift up and move on a bit further — press down again.' Harry demonstrated what he meant, moving quickly along the back bone to the neck which he felt between thumb and fingers. 'You see Davey, a good wide dock means a good finish, strong hindquarters and usually a nice full leg of mutton. As I move my hand up the back I feel for a level back bone, this gives strength and good carriage. Then at the neck I feel for a good thick neck well set on with no dip behind the shoulders.' I had another try and Harry smiled. 'That's more like it. The more you handle sheep the sooner you'll know what to feel for.'

'Why do you half shear, Harry?' I asked.

'So that the sheep look their best. I dress them up, if you like,' replied Harry. 'If I've got a ram a bit weak in the hindquarters then I'll leave a bit more wool on. Or one might have a bit of a dip in the back, I can level it off when I half shear. Mind you, a really good judge will spot it, but we try to best 'em. See those six ewes in the next pen?' I looked across. 'Try to imagine two pairs of three.' Harry pointed with his shears. 'I want each ewe in the three to be uniform with the others, that's length, height and face colour. You can see that I'm going to have to be very careful not to take too much wool off one — and not leave too much on another.'

Later on I watched Harry carry the dandifying process even further. The trimmed sheep were doused with a bloom dip which gave them a sandy colour. This was flicked on to the fleece with a distemper brush from a bucket of dip, then the whole fleece was combed. Harry got these combs from the woollen mills and mounted broad strips of the comb, whose tiny teeth were set in leather, onto a wooden frame which was shaped like a large butter pat. With these combs he teased and patted the fleece until it appeared solid, but as the sheep turned the fleece cracked and one could see right down to the pink skin. He spent literally hours in this process of preparing for show.

From time to time we would put halters on the rams and ewes to get them used to the idea of being led. Harry would walk them up to the concrete pathway in front of the sheep shed and then run them back, demonstrating the bouncing, corky gait of a good ram. Trying to get them to keep their heads up was a real effort, normally they loved to get their heads tucked right down and thus it was most difficult to teach them. Harry said that carriage in a ram was most important and breeders liked a ram with plenty of spirit.

'Which do you reckon is the best ram here Harry?' I asked.

'The one yer holding!' laughed Harry. 'He's got a perfect head — broad and yet not too long. See that lovely mouse colour on the nose — and no wool round his eyes or on the bridge of his nose. Big bright eyes and wool to his cheeks and the tips of his ears. We should do well with him.' Harry stood back and gazed at the ram. 'He's wide chested and deep, and ribs sprung like a barrel. I like him.'

Soon Harry was off round the shows and the collection of rosettes and prizecards grew. Each time he returned Edgar would ply him with questions, mainly about the other shepherds, many of whom he had known in years past. Edgar was back with the flock now. Ted had disappeared from the shepherding scene, though we sometimes saw him, charging about the farm with a horse and cart.

In July Harry and Edgar held a council of war and decided it was time to go through the flock and to cull any ewes that were unfit for further breeding. Harry had already selected the shearling ewes that he wanted to join the flock, he reckoned that about thirty-five to forty ewes would have to go out.

One fine afternoon we brought the flock up to the dipping pens and began to sort them out. Each ewe had to be turned and Harry and Edgar checked the teeth and the udder. It is obvious that a ewe must be sound in the udder.

Sometimes during the lambing season a ewe had contracted a form of mastitis, Edgar called this 'garget'. We had a few cases of this infection each lambing time and although we could cure it, with penicillin infused through the teat at the time, we often found that the milk tissue in the quarter that had been infected had been damaged to such an extent that the ewe would not be capable of rearing lambs in the future. Not only this, but there was always a danger that the trouble, though now dormant, might flare up again.

These ewes then were out on this count alone. Sometimes we found that a ewe had damaged a teat or in some cases the udder on barbed wire and we had odd cases where a teat had been nicked in shearing though happily this was very rare.

At the same time the teeth of each ewe were checked. Teeth are a rough guide, at least to within six months of the age of a sheep, but once a ewe is full mouthed, that is she has eight incisors at four years old, she may retain her teeth for another two or three years, before she loses any. I had better explain! Sheep have no incisors in the upper jaw — they have a hard pad — and this meets with the lower incisors as the ewe bites the herbage — the molars or grinding teeth lie at the back of the mouth, in the upper and lower jaw.

Lambs have milk teeth — small incisors — but at ten to fourteen months the centre two milk teeth are replaced by two permanent incisors. She is then a two tooth, as a two shear she will have four teeth, as a three shear, six, and finally as a four shear she will be full-mouthed with eight teeth. Of course, in the case of our flock, any doubt as to the age of a ewe — she still having eight teeth, could be settled by checking the ewe's ear number. The sorting was a fairly quick process, Harry checked the teeth and Edgar looked at the udders as I caught and turned the ewes. Any ewe to be culled, we paint marked across the back. Ewes that had lost incisors but were sound below were given one mark, ewes that were unsound below, that is in the udder, were marked twice.

Harry said when I questioned him about the marking

that the draft ewes had been given, that those full-mouthed but with unsound udders were sold as warranted correct in the mouth but unsound below. Any full-mouthed ewes that were sound in the udder went off as fully warranted; these included barren ewes and those being culled because of faults in fleece quality or conformation. Ewes that had lost incisors were called 'broken-mouthed'. We put the ewes culled out into Cherry Orchard and moved the flock back to Bean Meadow. Harry helped me to take the ewes over and on the way we passed the oats, rustling in the light wind and looking near to harvest. They stood with their red poppy banners flaming defiance and filling Willow Furlong with their brightness.

35. *Tupping*

The oats in Willow Furlong were cut at the beginning of August — they would stand in their stooks three clear Sundays before carting. A few poppies still lent a splash of colour against the hedgerow, in those days all corn was opened up with the scythe around the field and the head-land corn hand-tied.

'Time we flushed the ewes,' said Edgar. 'Then we can get the tups in.'

'What do you mean by flushing Edgar?' I asked.

'Well ye've seen 'ow we'da kip the ewes on pretty hard tack these last weeks?'

'Yes,' I agreed.

'Well, we'da put 'em on some good grub, say a week afore the tup goes to 'em. It do 'elp the ewes ter coom ter the tup — fer matin'. Harry sez it brings more twins too.'

At the end of the first week in August we took the flock up to the pens and sorted them out. Harry reckoned on fifty to a tup though when he was using a young tup — a shearling — he gave thirty.

We first sorted ten ewes and put them with the forty maiden ewes which were joining the flock, to steady them up for they were quite wild. Harry said, 'We don't want ter flush these, a single a piece would please me fine. Take them down to the old canal pasture David. We'll let them settle down there before we put the tup in. I'll use that old four shear tup when it's time. Never put a shearling ram with maiden ewes — neither know the ropes.'

I took my bunch along the top of the Common and down across Tunnel Field to the canal pasture, for the shearlings were a bit wild — but the older ewes in the bunch were steadier and knew the way and they had a steadying effect on the shearlings. By the time I got back from taking them with Owd Bob, Harry and Edgar had almost finished sorting.

Forty ewes had already been put out in Stone Field, where there was a rare bite of clover aftermath now that the hay had been taken off. The rest were split up into smaller groups, some in the Lizard, some in Pond Meadow, and so on. It was important that groups were kept separate, so that when we put the rams in, each would mind his own business and not go looking over the hedge. Harry said that sometimes three tups were put in with a much larger crowd of ewes, but never two.

'Two would spend ower much time fightin' but with three, one would allus be working,' said Edgar with a laugh.

With the flock scattered it meant a lot of walking and looking but I loved the break it gave me from the lamb fold and the routine work of pitching and hurdle carrying. I could now carry three — sometimes four — gate hurdles in my shirt sleeves, without getting sore shoulders. It was amazing how tough the skin and muscle on my shoulders had become, almost like a pad of hard flesh over the collarbone.

The first week passed, we had previously wormed the ewes and they were now clear. Harry called me up to the sheep house and we began to take the tups out. I noticed that he had kept a dozen ewes back from the flock and these were grazing in the big paddock above the chestnut paling pens.

'What's happening to those Harry?' I asked, pointing to the grazing ewes.

'Ah,' he said with an air of mystery. 'When we've got

these tups out, you can give me a hand with them — sort of an experiment you might say.'

We loaded three tups in the old van and bumped our way out to the first lot of ewes in Stone ground. Before leaving, Harry placed two large tins into the van and he spent several minutes searching around the woodpile for two long flat pieces of wood. He returned with two old pieces of gate hurdles. 'These will do the trick.' I murmured assent not really knowing what he was talking about.

On arrival in the field we carefully unloaded the first tup. This was one of Harry's own breeding and he was proud of it. 'Threw some topping lambs last year. I'll have two of his ram lambs to show next Summer' smiled Harry. 'Right, gently down. Whoa! Hold 'im. I've not finished with 'im yet.' He turned the ram and began inspecting its feet. 'They should be all right,' he said. 'A tup off his feet is no use at this time of the year. Fetch one of those tins of raddle and a stick.' I brought it across to him. 'Lift the lid off Davey.' I did so and Harry thrust in the stick and brought out a large dollop of thick yellow paint. This he plastered on the ram's chest and down between the fore-legs, explaining as he did so. 'This is raddle Davey. So that the tup marks every ewe he rides. Yellow is the first colour we put on. Now listen — the ewe's cycle of oestrus is sixteen days. He might tup, that's mate, with thirty of these ewes in that time, maybe ten. Now then, I'll take note of how many, then I'll change his colour — blue raddle next and he'll keep blue for the next sixteen days; then I'll follow that with a red raddle.'

'But,' I objected, 'What if he hasn't mated properly — the ewe will still be marked.'

'That's just it,' rejoined Harry. 'Those ewes will come into season again and the tup will mark them with the blue on top of the yellow. Each time I change the colour I note the number of ewes he has mated with for the first time and those that have "turned" as we say.'

I was all agog though as yet I hadn't any idea of what Harry was up to. When we reached the sheep house Harry sent me to bring in the dozen ewes and I penned them in one of the vacant pens. Meanwhile he was busy pitching a hole in the sloping turf, as I passed him he straightened up and said 'There I reckon that's deep enough. Go and fetch the stock — that we put the rams in when I'm gettin' 'em ready for show.'

Still puzzled, I lifted the stock from its socket and took it up to him. Harry set it firmly in the spot prepared, trod the earth down around it, and grinning at me said 'Now we'll see if there's life in the old dog yet!' Taking a halter we caught a ewe and led her up to the stock. It wasn't easy but with me behind and Harry in front pulling we managed. 'Face her down hill,' said Harry, and in she went. The piece of sacking came in handy again and with this over her head she stood quiet. 'Now for matey — come on.' Harry led the way down to one of the small pens. He swung open the door. Inside was the oldest ram I had ever seen. 'This is the best bred tup we've got, he's twelve and not much good on his legs,' said Harry, as I looked rather doubtfully at the little old hobbledy ram. 'Look at that colour and his head. I've handpicked those twelve ewes for him and we're going to try to mate him with them. Come on let's get started.'

So we led the old tup out and indeed he mated with all twelve ewes. Some of these held to him and out of eleven lambs he fathered, four ram lambs were eventually sold for export as stud rams to various parts of the world.

The following Spring old hobbledy died, but one of his sons entered our flock to carry on his line. 'Ah well I reckon 'eda shot 'is bolt afore 'e went ter glory!' cracked Edgar.

36. *The Little Foxes*

All day the Hunt had been around, they had 'found' in Furzen Wood quite early in the meet and the fox had taken them downwind, out and across Beau Meadow with hounds in full cry across the broad grass acres. Harry came down to the fold in the kale and gave me the news. 'I saw him across Aldbury road and strike out across the plough, his old tail was well up.' I had worked on in the wet kale, looking for night and the chance to get some dry clothes on. We were folding below the beech woods in a steep field which clung by its fingertips to the hillside. A mist came down on to the tops of the hills and closed me round with the hurdled lambs. From time to time I heard the deep belling of the hounds giving tongue, then silence would fall again as if smothered by the thickening mist. A woodpecker flew out of the beeches. I had seen nothing, but heard the thrum-thrum glide of his dipping flight as wing feathers beat the heavy air. From afar off — no, not so far off, the hounds gave frantic tongue.

Suddenly he was there — a dog fox, tongue lolling, plastered with yellow mud, his tail dragging like a loaded paint brush. Yellow slit eyes saw me, as he crawled through a hurdle, but he paid no heed. Straight through the lambs he went and out into the kale on the other side. I heard a yikkering in the tall kale and a young red fox ran down the far side of the netting — he was moving like light as he disappeared into the mist.

A couple of hounds broke cover followed by another and another, sterns well up and following the line. They lost it amongst the sharp tang of the sheepfold and nonplussed they cast below me. The huntsman appeared, his pink not so pink now but muddied and soaking, his mare lathered. He made to speak, but below us the hounds gave triumphant tongue and his horn went to his lips and away they went. Hounds, horses and riders spilled into the field and followed the sound. A young hound, obviously tired, came over to the corn bin and cocked a leg, then ambled off.

Down in Ash Copse the baying of hounds swelled to a wave of sound, to be cut off as cleanly as if a door had been slammed shut. The silence prickled with horror. Then the pack voices rose to a scream of terrible significance, amongst the grey ash poles steam rose from horses, worrying hounds and a broken fox, as death came swiftly to Ash Copse.

Later the muffled voices and slapping of horse flanks, muted hound voices, then the lift of the clear horn as the Hunt moved away and gave the day best, and the old fox that lay panting not far from me in the merciful kale — watching the tongues, not of the hounds, but of grey fog curling round the jungle of stalks.

It was a time-honoured custom amongst the men on the farm to stop whatever they were doing when the Hunt was near and to watch. Edgar, unlike most of the watchers, never betrayed the fox to the Hunt and I quickly learnt to do the same. 'Ees a 'gart enuff again 'im,' would grunt the old man. 'Let they 'ounds werk fer they keep.'

Several times near Cold Harbour we watched a hunted fox jump onto the farmyard wall and run along the coping stones before jumping into the crook of a great beech tree, then out along one of the long sweeping branches and down to the ground again, leaving the yarring hounds baffled for a few precious moments, until casting around they found his line again.

One morning, again near Cold Harbour, Edgar and I watched the fox running before the hounds. He was in no way stretched although the pack was not five minutes behind. Later we heard a real hullabaloo towards Frithsden Beeches and a quarter of an hour later the fox loped easily into the stackyard. He stopped by the gate and cocked a leg — moved on a few paces — then sat on his haunches and scratched an ear before resuming his leisurely way towards the Brick Kiln.

On more than one occasion I got the impression that the fox accepted shepherds and sheep as harmless, neutral, bystanders.

I remember whilst pitching hurdles with Edgar soon after the Hunt had met at Albury Cross, seeing a beautiful dog fox leap the hurdles and run amongst the sheep, sending them milling around, before darting away again through the kale. It happened so quickly that we were left gasping — there was no doubt that he saw us, obviously we did not count.

For a few weeks I looked after the poultry whilst one of the Land Girls was away. The poultry houses stood in the field near Home Farm and bordering the Common. Some of the hens had got into the annoying and dangerous habit of laying away, and my opening of the pop-holes in the morning was the signal for a spirited dash to the bracken by at least a dozen hens — from which they would emerge minutes later cackling in triumph. I was not the only one to have noted this habit, for one misty September morning one hen made a one-way trip to the bracken and a fox ran within a few feet of me, carrying a limp and lifeless hen.

I only once saw the results of a fox's blood lust. One evening the Land Girl forgot to lock up eighty White Leghorn X Rhode Island Red pullets. The next morning eighty white bodies lay scattered from Home Farm to Stoney Bottom, some headless, some with broken necks, only a few 'worried' in any way badly, but all dead.

Everyone on the farm had chicken and chicken again for dinner that week. At first I wondered whether the vixen from the earth amongst the larches in Stoney Bottom was responsible for the slaughter but Edgar said not. 'Tis very rare they do 'unt so near 'ome' was his brief comment. A few weeks later whilst walking in Furzen Wood I found the body of a vixen in full milk — she had been poisoned. We found her cubs eventually, blind and starving to death, teetering on little sticklike legs. It was far too late to do anything but the most merciful. I remembered Edgar's remark when telling me of the badger dig, 'Thars a lot worse things than they red coats!'

37. The Chair

At the end of November we began feeding the ewes crushed oats and nuts in the troughs and at night sweet hay to tempt them. They were feeding on rape and turnips during the day and running back on pasture at night. Edgar said that it was most important to keep the ewes fit but not fat, the more exercise they got the better. 'Iver sin us run ewes on the road, 'specially when we've 'ad snow. There be naught so bad as ewes heavy in lamb standing lookin' at one another.' The old man went on 'By the way Davey, I see ye've pitched a new fold on the rape and turnips. Afore ye let 'em out in t'mornin' pick out all the big turnips and bag 'em up. Harry'll be glad of 'em down at the sheep 'ouse. 'Ave sum yersel, they be rare an' sweet.'

'Why can't the ewes have them Edgar?' I asked.

'Too many roots baint any good ter ewes in lamb, they der throw big watery lambs. Ye'll allus 'ear sheep men say "Good root year — bad lambin' year",' said Edgar, nodding his head sagely.

The next morning I busied myself picking out the biggest turnips. Then Edgar came over to me 'Harry's cummin' up ter 'elp us wi' the chair. I'll give 'ee a lift in there.'

'What do you mean by the chair, Edgar?' I asked.

The old shepherd laughed 'Yer still a bit green Davey. Weda use the chair fer foot rottin' when ewes be too heavy ter turn. Ye'll see.'

We finished the turnips and instead of letting the ewes on, moved them back across the pasture into a collecting pen just beyond the field gate. At this point the cart track running between the fields was fenced on both sides. Someone had had the clever idea of hanging two gates across the track and these with the pasture gate and the old gate into Quarry Field opposite provided a pen with four exits. This proved extremely useful expecially when driving cattle or sheep on your own, by nipping ahead and setting the gates, the animals could be turned in the direction you wanted them.

Harry arrived in the van and without more ado lifted the chair out. It was a large rectangular frame on to which had been nailed a thick corn sack, the edges of which were firmly clamped down by a second but lighter frame of wood.

I gave him a hand to carry it across to the railings, noticing that two flat hooks of metal were screwed into the top of the frame. The chair was propped at an angle against the fence, the hooks dropping neatly over the rail behind. It was then I noticed two smaller hooks about the centre of each upright. Harry drew from his pocket a length of thick plaited rope one end of which he looped over one hook, letting the other end drop down. 'Righto Dave, you can catch for a bit, Edgar and I'll look over their feet,' called Harry.

As each ewe was caught it was eased backwards to the

chair and quietly tipped backwards into it, the braided rope passed quickly over its chest and fastened over the hook. The ewe lay stranded, unable to struggle and Harry and Edgar standing on either side, trimmed its feet. Some needed a fair bit of attention, others little more than a quick trim round with the knife. The famous ointment was there and later on, when Harry was called away by the bailiff, I helped Edgar with the feet. I was still chary of going too deep when I found a bad foot, but Edgar would snort as I made to put the ointment on 'It's no gud a'puttin' balm on un till ye've gart the bad out' and made me do a proper job, as he called it.

It was on this day that Edgar finally told me the secret of his balm. 'Keep it ter yersel' mind fer I'da knowed it fer years.' Quite simply it consisted of equal parts of copper sulphate and Stockholm tar mixed with Venice of Turps, plus a drop of Jeyes fluid. It was a fine ointment, tacky so that it stuck well to the foot and helped to grow a good, strong, yet pareable hoof.

38. Lambing Time

The leaves had gone but the embers of Autumn and the old year still burned in the bushes of thorn and briar. Redwings broke from their feasting on the bright berries, sometimes I was near enough to see their flame-coloured flanks and cream eyestreak as they flew up with a 'seep' of protest and let the wind scatter them like brown leaves.

I watched eagerly for a sight of the wax-wings but it was perhaps too early yet.

The lambing yard was already built and waiting, we had built it in good time in Cherry Orchard near the great beech tree.

'Damn sight too near I'm thinking,' said Harry. 'Never mind, p'raps it won't drip too much.'

It was a good site for all that, snug under the hill, with the farm and great house to the north of us. The line of the Common trees sheltering us from the West winds and the shoulder of the pasture hunched up to break the spite of the east. Southward the pasture ran gently down to a great 'bullfinch' hedge over which lay the sheephouse reached by a little wicket gate. Harry liked it being so handy to his cottage, and said he would be able to sleep at home this lambing. Edgar preferred to stay in the shepherd's hut, which was drawn up alongside the yard. 'As long as me old legs 'old up. Ida loike ter be 'andy,' growled the old man.

One gate led from Cherry Orchard into Duck Field which was down to kale and swedes. The far side had been sown with 'Hungry Gap' which we were told would stand the frost better even than Thousand Head kale. Duck Field was so named because it had a pond in one corner which always harboured a pair of mallard, and on early mornings I had often seen the grey heron standing patiently near the holly bush which stood overhanging the water.

I divided my day between old Edgar in Cherry Orchard seeing to the tegs and pitching the folds ready for receiving the first ewes and lambs in Duck Field. At first I saw very little of the lambing until one morning in mid-January. Edgar called me over to the hut. 'Harry be took bad — migraine or summat, kin 'ardly lift 's 'ead up. Bill gonna 'elp wi' the 'urdling, an' I wants 'ee along o' me wi' lambs.'

That was only the beginning, for I spent most of my days and nights from then on, in the lambing yard with Edgar. I fetched and carried for him seemingly non-stop for the next few weeks. Time became meaningless. All the pens were full — ewes and singles, ewes and twins, the odd set of triplets, a ewe that had lost her lamb — full of milk and blaring to let the world know.

In the morning I gave each pen clean water in the small buckets we used, lifted down their wooden feed boxes from the roof and fed the ewes with oats and nuts. I made sure each lamb was sucking and had its little belly full and, if not, made certain the ewe's teats were clear or not so swollen with milk that a weakly lamb could not suck.

Edgar would let the flock out and trough-feed the ewes outside the yard, keeping back any ewes that looked too near to lambing. An odd one or two would already be down in labour.

Then back to breakfast in the old hut by the blazing stove. Edgar lived sheep non-stop. 'Arter brakefust gie that long-headed ewe in the top pen wi' the single, a sprig of ivy. An' put some more salt licks roun' t' pens Davey,' said the old man. 'If that ole ewe in t' yard near t' barn, lambs a single, we'll give 'er one o' they triplets ter mother.'

After breakfast I fetched the ivy, cast my eye round the pens and gave those that needed them new mineral salt licks, these slotted into holders fixed to the bale wire at the rear of the pens.

Edgar was kneeling by the ewe he had mentioned. 'Fetch I the lambin' oils Davey. Wert! Doanee rush. Wark soft. Iver told 'ee afore.'

When I returned the shepherd had his sleeve rolled up. He clenched his fist and said 'Pour some ower me fingers an' t' back o' me 'and. Tisn't much, she's gart a single wi' both legs back, soon put that roight.' I could see the lamb's nose in the passage. 'Stop strainin' yer silly owd bitch,' said Edgar. With a gentle easy movement he slipped his hand over the lamb's nose. 'I be feelin' fer the crown of the 'ead. Then I moves me 'and till I feels the shoulder.' His face lit up. 'Gart un. Now I'der foller it roun' till I'der feel the foot. Mind yer I der kip me 'and tight close ter the lamb, wi' me fingers together. Na I waits till the owd vool stops strainin', cups the foot in the palm o' me 'and an' draws un forrard. There!' A black hoof lay alongside the lamb's twitching nose.

'Davey, while I der git the other foot forward, go an' git the little tacker in they set o' triplets. But mind yer, doan let this ewe see un.'

I brought the triplet lamb carefully round the back and knelt by Edgar. 'Na I der show 'ee summat,' he grunted. With firm but gentle pressure he pulled on the two legs with one hand and at the same time held the head, gripping the lamb round the back of the neck. He waited until the ewe strained and then pulled. First the head was born — the ewe cried and he let her rest a moment — then as she began to work again the chest and body slipped easily into the world. Immediately Edgar said 'Hold 'er down Davey, doanna let 'er up.' He seized the triplet lamb and smothered it in the waters which had burst on birth of the ewe's own lamb. Then he rubbed the two lambs together, scraping off the thick yellow fluid that streaked the new lamb's body and rubbing it into the triplet.

'Roight' breathed Edgar. 'Let's see what she da think!'

He drew the foster-lamb-to-be round by the forelegs and laid it by the ewe's nose. Immediately she began to croon and lick the foster lamb, which struggled in the threads of the water bag (which had preceded the birth of her own lamb). 'Grand,' said Edgar and drew her lamb forward.

We left them both bleating and stumbling around as she, proud mother of 'twins', got on with the job of washing them clean.

Edgar was already walking towards the pens. He stopped by a lambless ewe, still calling for her lamb. 'We'll try a lamb on 'er. Moight be ower lucky day. She be full o' milk.' The old man scratched his head, pushing his battered trilby back as he considered. 'Tell 'ee what Davey, that ewe at the end. She gart a big un an' a little un. We'll try the little tacker on this un.' He turned to me. 'Gart yer knife?' I felt hopefully in my pockets. 'What 'ave I told 'ee. Allus carry yer knife. Here yar!' He thrust his own towards me. 'Ida put this un's dead lamb top o' they bales, inna sack. Tak it ter the 'ut an' skin un, then bury the lamb.'

Skinning was the work of a few minutes and leaving the skin on the bench, I took the body over to the lime pit. Edgar always insisted upon the yard and surrounding field being kept clean. Even when a ewe lambed down in the field, he made sure afterbirth or cleansing was gathered up and buried. 'No use arskin' fer trouble then a' grumblin' when yer gets it. Taint only disease yer see but they old varxes cum aroun' a' nights. It be a small step from cleansin's ter lambs.' I'd just thrown a shovel of lime in when Edgar hailed me. 'Cum on Davey, I be ready ter put the jacket on this feller.' He held up the lamb, not swinging it by the forelegs, which he had once told me off for doing, but couched in his arms. He had told me that when a lamb is held solely by the forelegs, all the weight hangs upon them and the rib case is squeezed, this Edgar said could be very harmful to a young lamb.

Back at the hut Edgar had taken up his knife and was piercing holes in the skin. He looked up. 'Glad ye had sense ter leave the tail on un — that's the first place she'll smell.' I held the lamb whilst Edgar first rubbed the skin all over its face, neck and chest, then bending its legs we eased them through the holes in the skin. Finally we tied the skin in front of the chest and under the belly. 'That should do un,' said Edgar. 'Let's see what the old gel thinks of 'im.'

We walked over to the yard and Edgar dropped the lamb gently into the pen. 'Get ready ter take the lamb out if sheda go fer it.' The ewe backed away stamping her front feet, the lamb a little hampered by the skin, hobbled towards her. The ewe was still suspicious. Edgar said quietly, 'Go fetch Bob from sheep 'ouse.'

'Owd Bob,' I said wondering what on earth Bob had to do with it.

'Yes, yer booby!' snapped the old man.

I returned a few minutes later rather breathless with Bob on the leash and called to Edgar from the gate of the lambing yard. The old man beckoned 'Good lad, keep 'im close and come 'ere.' I moved along the line of pens, Edgar had lifted the lamb out again. 'Roight,' he said. 'When I puts the lamb in, bring Owd Bob right up ter the 'urdle an' let the ewe see 'im.' He lowered the lamb once more into the pen. I brought Bob up — the result was startling enough. The ewe charged right at the hurdles, so violently that she nearly caught my fingers resting on the top rail. The lamb was knocked sideways — instinctively the ewe moved between the fallen lamb and the dog as the youngster struggled to regain its feet in the straw. Again I brought Bob close, this time she backed into the far corner of the pen, the lamb at her side, and turning she nuzzled it and spoke in that voice all shepherds love to hear. Seconds later the lamb was sucking and we walked out of the yard, well pleased and ready to look round the ewes in the field, Edgar carrying a satchel over his shoulder and his crook.

All seemed peaceful amongst the ewes. 'Allus watch fer a ewe off on 'er own,' said Edgar as we walked up the field. He pointed with crook, 'See that un in t'fer corner.' I saw the ewe walking up and down beside the hedge. As I watched she laid down, only to get up again.

'She seems very restless Edgar, I thought I saw some white behind her,' I said excitedly.

'Ye did,' growled the old shepherd. 'She be a shearling an' I bet my boots she's got the head out.'

As we walked over he explained. 'With a shearling ye never know what ter expect — nor do she! When she start's a'workin' and the head is through, she'da think its all over. I'ver sin lambs strangled like that, cos she'da roam around and won't settle ter work agin.'

Edgar put his hand on my arm. 'Whoa a minute. She be gettin' down agin. Creep up soft Davey and see if ye can 'old 'er.'

I moved quietly towards the ewe, approaching her from behind and catching her without any bother. Edgar came up and slowly knelt beside me. His legs seemed to be worse than ever. 'Ye can lamb this un Davey. Shearlin's be too small fer me, 'member I tellin' 'ee that yourn were real shepherd's 'ands. Ye mus' start sometime. I'll 'elp 'ee.'

I knelt beside the ewe, on the folded sack we always carried when going round the flock. The ewe on her side — belly against my knees. Her head to my right, so that my left hand and arm with sleeve rolled right up was free to work. Edgar would have worked the other way on, as he was right-handed. I clenched my fist and he poured on the lambing oils. 'Roight Davey, once ye start ye've gotta finish. Tain't no good messin' about. If ye stop an' leave 'er, she'll swell up in t'passage an' thas in a worser mess than afore. Slip yer 'and in over the lamb's 'ead.' I did so and was surprised at how easily my hand moved. The ewe started to strain. I waited until she relaxed and started to move my hand again. 'Good lad,' breathed Edgar. 'Work with 'er. Move yer 'and down topside o' the lamb and feel the shoulder.'

'Got it,' I said.

'Can ye feel the leg?' said Edgar. I felt the leg, it was straight back and moving along it I felt the hoof.

'I've found the foot Edgar.'

'That's it,' he smiled. 'Now keep the foot in yer palm

110

an' close yer fingers roun' it an' draw yer 'and out.' I began to move. 'Slow na,' said Edgar. 'Wait till she stops pushing.' Then the foot was beside the lamb's chin. 'She'll cum na,' said Edgar. 'Wi' one foot an' the 'ead. That lamb's bin too long a'comin' anyways.'

I drew on the one leg and the back of the lamb's neck and drew it out and down in a curling movement, as I had seen Edgar do. 'That's it — niver draw un out straight — taint natrell.'

This lamb lay rather limp and floppy and Edgar gave it a brisk rub down with a wisp of straw, then slapped it. The lamb cried, and Edgar gave it to the ewe to mother, but not before he had painted the navel cord with iodine. ' 'elps ter dry it up,' he explained. 'Not ser likely ter get joint ill.'

'We'd best look round the others,' said Edgar. 'When she's cleaned it up, we'll 'ave 'er back in a pen.' Nothing was stirring, though Edgar said that quite a number of ewes had 'dropped' — that is, the lamb had moved down in the abdomen, which was a sure sign that lambing was very near. Before we stopped for dinner we had several lambs in the lambing yard to inject — they had to be done within twenty-four hours of being born — to protect against lamb dysentery and pulpy kidney. 'This is a job ye can take on if ye likes,' said Edgar. 'Jes' make sure ye give each lamb a paint mark, so's we know they be done.' He showed me how to slip the needle into the loose skin on the inside of a hind leg. On this particular afternoon we got the ewes in early. 'I der smell snow,' said Edgar. Certainly it had become very dark, the grey lowering clouds had an ominous yellow tint in the South East. Before darkness fell the first flakes were drifting on the wind.

We fed round the pen and saw to all the sheep's needs. I went out and brought in to the comfort of the lambing yard the single lamb I had lambed, together with another pair of twins.

Edgar looked round the yard. 'We'll be needing nigh on twenty pens ter night Davey. Let's empt' un na, afore we 'as our tea. I shoulda thought afore I'da brought t'ewes in. Niver mind we kin do it.' One by one all the ewes and lambs that were thriving were pushed into the larger half-covered pens. We missed the Dutch Barn of other years.

'If it gits real bad we'll 'ave ter use part of the sheep 'ouse,' said Edgar. We had one more ewe to help before going for tea. The ewe had lambed a single without any bother but she was still restless. Edgar felt her. 'She's gotta another an' she can't get un away. I'll have a feel.' Almost immediately he said, 'Lamb's backside first an' it's a big un. I'll take it that away.' Skilfully he brought the back legs round into the passage and the lamb with the ewe's help was ushered into the snowy world. Edgar bent over it clearing away the mucus that covered the mouth and nostrils. 'Canna hang about wi' they,' he explained. 'They do swallow ower much fluid cummin' backwards. Though ye gotta be easy, as the lungs git pushed up agin the ribcage.'

He took a clean piece of straw and gently pushed it up the lamb's nose — the lamb gave a great sneeze. 'That be better,' said the old man. The lamb cried and its breathing which had been very gulpy and spasmodic settled down to a steady rhythm. We passed a ewe with one lamb and started if off sucking. 'Lambs need warm milk right away, once they be cold in this weather, they be gonnas.'

Tea at long last. Edgar made for the hut. I headed away over the Common for home in the village, promising to be back straight away for the night. It was still snowing, great flakes lazily swaying this way and that through the darkness, as if each were choosing where to settle.

39. *The Great Snow*

Indoors the fire blazed and gleaming brasses on the dresser winked in the play of firelight. It would have been good to settle by the fire for the night but up there on the hill Edgar was alone and anyway I felt excited at the prospect of a night in the lambing yard. Uncle Henry, as I had come to call my landlord, took his cornet down from the shelf, Auntie Sybil made for the kitchen; and pulling on an extra jersey and another pair of knee-length socks, I wrapped my greatcoat round me and headed for the yard. I crossed the Common in the silence that snow brings, so quiet I could hear the snow settling on the brambles below the thorn trees.

'There's five lambed Davey. Iver drawn 'em back under the bales, but we'll 'ave ter pen they.' Edgar greeted me with this news as I came up the steps into the hut. ''ave a cuppa tay an' then we'll fettle 'em.'

The yard was quiet. Edgar stood by the thatched hurdles and spoke to the ewes. 'Coom me dames. Coom me dames.' The sky had cleared and the stars burned fiercely. Edgar switched on the great lambing torch and called again. 'Roight, we'll 'ave a look. Walk soft mind!' Ruby eyes shone in the beam, not a ewe moved. We walked through them and at times stepped over them, but they knew Edgar. We penned the five ewes, three singles and two sets of twins. They were all hale and hearty save one of the twins. Its mate was pint-sized, but already sucking, the other was a large, big-bodied lamb and had obviously been some time coming into the world. Edgar held the ewe against the hurdles whilst I tried to get some milk into the lamb. Time and again I put it against the teat but it just couldn't get the idea. Every time I let go it staggered to the wrong end!

'Daft thing,' I exclaimed, blowing on my frozen fingers.

'Try squirtin' sum milk down un,' said Edgar, easing his bent back. At first I got the milk anywhere but the right place, but at last the lamb got a mouthful. It fastened onto the teat and its little tail wagged furiously, 'Got 'im,' laughed Edgar. 'It'll be aroight na, once it's tasted the milk, it'll find un agin. We'll go an' 'ave a warm.'

An hour later I went out again, all was quiet in the yard. When I got back and told the old man, he said 'If nowts astir be midnight then they do generally go till first light.'

At eleven o'clock Edgar came back with the news that four or five were making their bed and that we were going to be busy. Ewes before lambing are restless, they select a spot, paw the ground, walk round and round it, lie down, get up, lie down again before settling to labour. Edgar

113

called this 'making their bed'. 'We'll give 'em time ter git on with it. No sense interfering unless they needs 'elp an' we'll know that soon enuff,' he said.

Just after midnight the sky closed in, it seemed milder, and the snow began to fall again, with a steadiness and persistency that boded no good. There was little wind and at the moment drifting was slight. In the yard four ewes had lambed, the fifth, a shearling, was walking about with the water bag out and showed no sign of settling. 'Catch 'er Davey an' ye can 'ave a look.' She had a lamb coming backwards and I lambed it that way, with very little trouble, and remembering Edgar's trick, I used the straw to make it sneeze and clear its nostrils.

We got them all under cover — several ewes were now showing signs of lambing. 'By gum Edgar they have picked a real night for it.'

He laughed, 'Aye an' do you see what colour they are — blues! Remember that tup takin' thirty that night in Canal Field! These be sum o' yourn Davey.'

The snow outside the yard was getting deeper. Edgar didn't moan but I could see that his legs were giving him a lot of trouble. 'If you like Edgar, I'll see to them and call you if I need help.' I made the suggestion guardedly, knowing how proud the old man was, but he turned towards me.

'Good lad, me legs is fair playin' up. I'll git on ter bunk fer a bit arter we've 'ad a cup.'

It was three o'clock when I hit trouble. She was an oldish ewe, thank heaven. I had been watching her for a bit, but she just could not get on with it, though she tried hard and cried out in her struggle.

The other ewes were safely lambed and penned, all seemed well except for this one. I hesitated about starting — it was so different with Edgar at my side. I went over to the hut, the top of the door was ajar, to let out any fumes from the stove. I peered in, Edgar was dead to the world. Light from the stove shone on his sparse grizzled hair. I hadn't the heart to wake him, and taking the satchel I went plodding back to the yard. The ewe lay in the open so I pushed her back under cover of the thatched hurdle

114

roof which ran along one wall of the yard. I had plenty of elbow room and at least it was dry overhead. The ewe lay very quiet. I propped the lambing torch to shine on her, took off my coat and rolled my left sleeve right back. Then I gave my hand and arm a liberal coating of lambing oil and started work. I knew in my heart that I was committed. Edgar had said time and again, 'Don't start unless you mean to finish.' I waited for the ewe to relax, then moved my hand in. I felt a leg in the passage and with mounting confidence followed the line. No head, there must be. I went back to the foot. Yes, it was the right way up, it was a front leg. I moved carefully round. Edgar had said that there was a fag paper's difference between life and death for the ewe, I must keep my fingers on the lamb. Good. I had the neck, and an ear and the eyes. The head of this lamb had fallen back. I eased the foreleg up the passage to give myself room to bring the head round. Praying for eyes in my fingers. Waiting until the ewe had stopped pushing. Glory be! The head came round and with my fingers behind the crown I drew it into the passage. I knew now by touch that this was not the only lamb, judging by the number of different legs there were three lambs. So I took the risk and drew the first lamb out head and foreleg. It slipped easily into the world once the head was born and I whisked it round to the ewe's nose. In again, I found a foot, but the head nearest did not belong. The ewe was straining more frequently now. My hand ached and my knuckles were bruised. I concentrated on the second head, my arm now at the full stretch, slipping over the crown I found the shoulder and a leg belonging. The lamb moved forward, and the head kept coming. I took the second leg into my hand and found the other shoulder, at last! I had the second lamb on the way and within seconds it, too, lay in the cold inhospitable world of snow. Mother ewe was still washing the first lamb and steam rose in the night air. I went back for the third, which was surprisingly large, and delivered it breech first to cut the time down. I drew them both round, the cords breaking naturally as I did so, and the triplets lay in the lamplight, floppy-eared, struggling and steaming as they tried to find their wobbly legs.

I wasn't going to tell Edgar, but I could not keep it in. I knew that he was pleased — not because he said much, but by the way he looked and the way he told Harry 'Davey delivered they hissel'.'

When the Head Shepherd returned to the yard, the end of that first week, the first snow lay a foot deep. Then came bright sunshine but a bitter wind, which denied any warmth. The frosts at night grew worse and in the sheltered places where any thaw had taken place during the daylight hours, the frost took hold again, driving deeper and deeper into the ground.

Three weeks later the snow was still there, not so white, not so much, as if it had shrivelled. The badger jaws of frost hung on like the grim death they were. Already the birds were suffering terribly. Walking home across the Common I found thrushes frozen to the lower branches of the thorn bushes where they had gone to roost and to sleep forever. Taking the cover off the hay bales in the early morning I found bluetits huddled in death beneath the canvas.

The water barrel froze solid and we had the extra chore of bringing water in milk churns from the dairy.

At night the lambing continued and in the morning we would see the pad marks of foxes all round the outside wall of the yard.

Edgar looked at the sky when I said that the thaw must soon come. 'Aye — 'pears so, but when snow lies on the hills it beckons fer more. We've gart a lot more of that there white stuff ter cum.'

He was right, the iron hand of the frost relaxed a little and the snow came, howling out of the ice house of the North as if a numberless pack of white hounds had suddenly snapped the leash. Edgar and I sat in the hut and listened to it shrieking across the field. Teeth of ice that cut and numbed our faces till they ached, as we stumbled our way over to the lambing yard.

The ewes kept the yard fairly clear — walking round. The snow outside was so deep that Harry began to worry about the ewes. 'They'll be getting that snow sickness.'

This is caused by several factors, snow or moss sickness occurs in poorly fed hill sheep when the unborn lambs drain away nutrients and protein that the ewe needs for her own daily functioning, but snow sickness can also hit ewes in a flock like ours, when they lack exercise and stand about.

'Harry,' said Edgar, 'take that fence down 'gain the beech tree, if we clear a track we can push the ewes out onto the Common road, that be kep' clear o' snow.' This is what we did and when the snow finally let up we were able to run the ewes out and back to get the exercise so vital to them.

Many roads were now impassable due to the colossal drifts. New tracks sprang into being, tractors and trailers keeping to the frozen ground from which the wind had blown the snow. I found myself walking with Tom the pony drawing the shepherd's float along the top of the bullfinch hedge, which had been bowed over by the weight of snow. When we reached a gateway I sank to my armpits pretty near and we just floundered across to the next bit of hedge. In some places snowdrifts were almost up to the telegraph wires.

One morning Billy went out to his sheep at Dan East Wood and found only an expanse of snow, not a hurdle, not a sheep in sight. His only clue to where the sheep were was the two tine fork, sticking up above the white wilderness. Harry and I went to help him, it was the first and last time I had to dig a fold out! We found the sheep all packed together along the line of hurdles, none the worse for wear, but very hungry.

In Duck Field the grey heron had caught his last fish. I found him with his yellow-green legs broken in a grip that was stronger and more terrible than his own.

The beech tree standing guard over the yard was constantly growing and shedding black starling leaves, as they fought and jostled like ragged urchins round the sheep troughs. Now and again amongst the quieter chaffinches I saw the black and chestnut bramblings, with their white rumps, searching, ever searching, for food beneath the beech trees.

A stranger came to the Common and added to the terror of the small birds. I saw him perched on the wires near the sheep house. In plumage of black, grey and white, the Great Grey Shrike, mean and evil in his beauty. Lapwings no longer lifted in changing patterns of black and white above the empty fields. They had long ago sought the mud flats and tidal reaches in their search for food, but beneath the drifted snow which smothered the kale, rabbits and hares ate and ate. Judging by the narrow racing tracks about the entrance holes they, too, had their troubles, for the stoats and weasels were not long in finding them out.

At night in the lambing yard we heard ominous crack-ings in the great beech, as branches embalmed in ice cracked under the weight.

So the weeks dragged by, all life seemed held in the grip of numbing cold. Somehow work amongst the sheep went on, we learnt to adapt to the weather. We lost lambs, for we always lost lambs at lambing time, but not so many as we had feared. Once a carrion crow came to the yard in broad daylight and took the eyes of a lamb newly born. Harry brought his twelve bore up to the hut, but the crow did not pay us a second visit.

Now and again an inexperienced shearling dropped her lamb out in the middle of the yard at night and wandered off, death for the lamb in the intense cold was very swift; this occurrence, thank goodness, was rare indeed, but we always blamed ourselves. Daily we drove the ewes out into the lane and gave them a brisk walk, then back to the fold and a feed of hay and mangolds.

It was my job to fetch the mangolds and it was an experience I shall never forget. I used to take Tom with the shepherd's float. Somebody in a dull-witted moment had opened the clamp at the weather end and although the hole had been packed with straw bales, these were of little defence against the searing cold from the North. I had to burrow into the clamp about twelve feet, throwing back the frozen mangolds to the outside. It seems hard to believe now, but I even lit a candle in my shaft and brought out the good mangolds two at a time on the fork. I shall never forget the light glistening upon the frozen jewels of moisture, which hung from the gold, orange and amber orbs.

The snow lasted until late March and never did a Spring-time come more welcome to the land, nor grass look greener to both shepherds and stockmen.

40. *The Hollow*

Bluebells came back to the Hollow and stood in azure ranks below the curtsying thorn. Cuckoos came and called again from hedgerow sycamores and towering elms. In fresh fields the hurdle lines traced new patterns upon the map of earth. Edgar, Harry, Jim and myself went about tending the flock, following the ceaseless cycle of the year: the sheep shaped our lives, the weather checked or speeded up our rhythm, but in the end we lived for the flock and were content.

Rabbits mowed the green rides through the Hollow and often blue smoke from tinkers' fires rose from The Flat, whilst their ponies grazed and various multicoloured garments were strewn over the bramble patches like strange, exotic flowers. On a May morning the torrent of birdsong rose and fell like a fountain of sound. Every rail, fence post and branching spray seemed to hold its chorister. At the height of the dawn chorus thrushes and blackbirds sat in the road and sang, so that I had to cycle round them on my way to work.

Four pairs of nightingales were nesting in the Hollow, nor kept their singing for the hours of night, but joined until the sun was high above the green bowl, with black-cap's liquid song, thrushes, blackbirds, the anvil-striking call of the great-tit, the chiffchaff's two-bit theme, and always the soft, sweet, bell cadences of the willow-warbler. Once I mentioned it to Edgar. 'Ah,' he said, 'I do loike to 'ear they.' No more than that, but then Edgar was never a man to go into raptures.

He never mentioned God. The nearest he got to it was one night in the lambing yard, when after a hard battle he brought a lamb to cry beneath the stars — 'Ida loike ter get one o' they bloody atheists ter stand 'ere na,' growled Edgar as he wiped his hands on the sack and painfully got to his feet.

41. *'That's my Fork'*

The first time I went haymaking I learnt a lesson. I was sent to join the gang of men in Pond Meadow, they were putting the hay into cocks, a thunder-storm was brewing and every pair of hands was needed to make the hay safe. I went up the field after dinner. I was early, the men were still sitting under the hedge. I plumped down next to Archie. 'Hullo young 'un. Ker. . . ker. . . kum to gi. . . gi. . . give,' Archie brought his hand down on his knee with a tremendous thwack, 'give us a hand.'

'Yes, Archie. Look, Bert's got his old turnip out, it must be time.'

The words were hardly out of my mouth when Bert heaved himself to his feet. 'There's thunder not far off. T'old pheasants are sounding off in Dan East Wood and the trees look as black as the inside of a bag. Let's get to it lads.'

Standing against the field gate were a row of hay forks. One by one as the men packed their bait tins away, they took a fork and shouldering it moved into the rows of hay. I followed suit, picked up a fork, and followed them. An indignant voice shouted after me, 'Hey! Hey! That. . . that. . . that's my f. . . for. . . for. . . fork.' I turned. Archie was waving a hay fork at me.

'What's wrong Archie? I didn't know it was your fork.'

Archie grinned sheepishly. 'Well it is and then again it isn't. Yer, yer, yer see, I. . . I. . . I. . . (thwack his hand came down on his thigh) I've made it mine through these last four Summers. I know the feel of it. I'd ner. . . n. . . know it in the d. . . d. . . d. . . (thwack) dark.'

I took the fork he held out to me and I handed his over. As I worked that afternoon I saw very clearly what Archie meant. His fork had become an extension of himself. He worked easily, and surely, with a deftness I envied. I was clumsy and awkward. I knew what I wanted to do, but I lacked the touch. I hadn't yet made the fork my own, but I would, given time.

In May the swifts came back and took up their screaming circus around the grey church tower. It was as if they had never been away. The nightingales sang not only at night from the hawthorns around the green Hollow, but throughout the flower laden days; vying with the songs of songthrush, blackcap (the mock nightingale) and the ever sweet contraltos of many a blackbird.

My measure of green days was empty, run dry. I left for the Army on May 18th, 1944.

OXFORDSHIRE

1. *Glympton Park*

In June of 1946 I was released from the Army on Class B, the condition being that I returned to work on the land. The weeks dragged their feet, the city seemed alien. Folk were tired of the War and returning soldiery were a reminder. I got the impression that they wanted to forget. I was glad to get on the train to take me down to Oxford. In my absence, Mr. A.P. Good had sold his estate at Northchurch and bought Glympton Park near Woodstock. I was to rejoin the farm staff down there.

Only one mishap occurred on the journey. We stopped at Birmingham and as I gazed idly out of the window, I saw a bicycle leaning against a post. The bicycle was painted silver. Quite smart, I thought; my eyes moved to the handlebars, they were covered with blue insulating tape. It was just like my bike. Dammit, it was my bike! I hurtled out of the train. A porter had inadvertently unloaded it from the guard's van and I spent another hour and a half waiting for the next train to Oxford.

I cycled the twelve miles to Glympton and was surprised to meet Eileen Berry at the top of the lane which led down to the village. She was working at a farmhouse near the Chipping Norton road. Apparently George Berry and Harry Fawkes had moved with their families to Glympton. Old Edgar, too, had come along, and when I got down to Harry's cottage, where I was to lodge, there he was, and it was a delight to see him again.

The year of 1946 was disastrous for the harvest. It never seemed to stop raining. I remember one field of oats in particular, we had to cut nearly every sheaf-band to dry out the corn.

We spent a lot of time carting muck out between the rows of stooks. There was nothing else to do. It was a year that convinced many farmers of the advantages of combine harvesters. Corn didn't have to be bone-dry. A couple of hours of sunshine and combines could go straight on with the job. The corn was in the bag and there was time to dry the corn in the dryer.

I gradually got used to the Oxfordshire dialect and being referred to as 'you'. 'Waddyer think o' that you?' or the triumphant yell as Alfie waved aloft a rabbit he had just dispatched with his 'thumping' stick in the harvest field. 'That be a rare capture you!'

When the men were busy 'chewing the fat' about goings on in the village, they often referred to so and so being 'proper dummel', a word that I had never come across before. Alfie told me what it meant. 'We do talk about hay when there's no sun in it as dummel,' he said. 'Tis dull and lifeless like, ye can't do much wi' it. Now hay wi' the sun in it is bright an' lively, slips from the fork in a twink, then tis ready fer makin', I reckon.'

The men's talk at bait time was never vindictive and after my life in the Infantry the almost total absence of four letter words, was striking. Life and death and the courting and mating that come between are topics that concern all men and snippets of information and conjecture filled the lunch hours. Alfie would tell us between mouthfuls, 'Know the courting couple I'da told 'ee of las' week.'

'Aye,' came the chorus.

'Well, theyda bin in the dell 'ole agin this arternoon.'

'Reckon they weren't seekin' bluebells you,' chortled Tom.

'Not they,' rejoined Alfie. 'They was two hours in there, could've picked well nigh a wood full, but theyda come out empty 'anded.'

'Hah!' the great trumpet guffaw came from Bill the Waggoner. 'Ida bet the lass didn't!'

My habit of always carrying a book in my bait bag soon caused comment. Edgar had said 'Readin' they books won't git yer bread 'n butter, Davey.' The farm men were of the same opinion. The idea of a grown man reading poetry beggared description. Alfie's verdict was typical. 'A few days paddlin' about wi' muck to yer eyebrows ud soon knock that nonsense out yer noddle. Take all yer time ter kip uproight!' Yet books on birds or butterflies brought a different reaction. Nothing much was said, apart from a sparse comment such as 'They be rare picktures' but hardly a day passed afterwards without someone trying to describe a bird they had seen. Alfie, the ploughman, and George, the pigman, were for ever producing grubby matchboxes from their capacious pockets, with the question, 'Waddyer reckon ter this un Davey'. At first the specimens were squashed and tattered having been well and truly swatted but gradually after I had explained what I wanted they would bring almost perfect specimens — alive into the bargain. Poplar Hawk Moths, Burnished Brasses with their gleaming wings, Ghost Swifts which danced amongst the long meadow grasses on Summer evenings, and the Gothic Arches with their beautifully veined wings. One lunchtime Alfie produced half a dozen Puss Moth caterpillars. 'Mind how yer touches 'em Davey,' he said, carefully opening his bait tin. 'Theyda got terrible stings on 'em, more like they scorpeens!' As the tin opened the men gasped at the sight of the green monsters with their pink and black cat faces and raised spiky tails from which waved vivid red whips.

The lanes of Oxfordshire were blessed with tremendously wide verges. I often heard them called 'the long acre' and some of the old men said that they dated from the time of stage-coaches and other horse-drawn traffic. 'No metal on't roads then yer see, come Winter an' plodging mire, they kep seekin' a better road an' so the track got wider an' wider.' I must have looked rather sceptical. 'Tis a fact you,' spat Old Henry, then shook his head sorrowfully, 'Can't tell these young uns nothin''.

2. 'Our Glad'

September slipped by and left the bright chestnuts to shine amongst the yellow-fingered leaves upon the village green. In the early morning I would see them before the children went to school, by evening they were gone, crammed into pockets, strung upon strings, but never so beautiful as when they lay in the early morning grass with the sun catching them. In October Jim came to live at Long Heath on the far side of the estate. A shepherd of Edgar's school, they had worked together before on the Hampshire and Wiltshire Downs, long seasons ago when they had looked after flocks on the wide, sheep mown pastures and heard the sheep bells call through the mist before the sun was up.

The Monday after Jim arrived, Edgar sent me up to Long Heath. 'I want yer to take a load of wire an' 'urdles up to Long Heath,' he said. 'Arter brakesfus'll do. Jim be a'goin' ter start pitchin' a fold on the rape and turnips. Ye can stay with 'im till dinnertime an' give 'im a hand settin' out.' He paused then, 'Don't worry 'bout 'im noddin' 's 'ead. 'e were shell-shocked in the fust warr — allus bin like it sin I'da knowed 'im.'

It was a bright morning with the elm trees splashed like yellow paint on the blue sky. Tom the white pony pulled the swaying load with a will and soon I arrived at Long Heath.

Jim had seen us coming up the long track and was waiting by the garden gate of his grey stone cottage. He came towards me as I reined in, smiling a greeting 'Ye'll be Davey, shepherd said he'd be sending you.' As he spoke his head nodded violently, to stop as he finished speaking. 'We'll have two nets off at the corner — a twenty-five and a fifty yarder an' fifty stakes.' The grey head nodded again 'Glad!' he yelled, turning towards the cottage. A young woman came down the path. She wore an old tweed coat — long and snagged by wire in many places. It was buttonless but bound round her by a leather belt. Her feet were encased in rubber boots. She walked bent forward so that her long black hair all but veiled her face. I caught one searing glimpse of an angry crimson welt which covered one side of her face from temple to chin — a birth mark. 'This be Glad, me daughter,' jerked Jim, 'She's allus bin wi' me and the sheep. Can't talk but there's no harm in 'er.'

We dropped the two nets. Glad began to put out the stakes, leaning them against the nets in perfect order. In next to no time, all the nets were dropped each with their stakes. All shepherds have a particular set of stakes for each net. There are hook nets and threadle nets — high and low respectively. Glad sorted the stakes with uncanny precision. Then we unloaded the hurdles dropping them in threes across the rape and turnips between the nets. Glad was ready propping three hurdles with one stake and leaning the appropriate stakes against them. So that when we started to pitch the line of hurdles, everything was within easy reach.

Wherever Glad went, Jim's black collie followed, and when we stopped for a cup of tea and a smoke under Heath Wood, the dog lay at her feet. During the next two seasons, whilst I worked with the flock, I saw much of Jim and 'Our Glad'. She never spoke. Sometimes we would see her on a misty morning, carrying out hurdles in chest-high kale, sodden with rain. Often in the evening light, with the sky all rose and gold behind the corn stacks, we would hear Jim's voice calling 'Home Glad.' Never an answer, but in our mind's eye we would see that stooping figure turn from the field and follow Jim home, followed in turn by the collie that seemed her shadow. I suppose to some it must have seemed an empty, brutish life. Yet to see Glad working day long amongst the sheep, with no clock but the sun, was to glimpse a tranquillity and peace that few possess.

Then again at lambing time — one wondered whether there wasn't some other language far more eloquent than our own, that Glad used as she tended the nursing ewes and lambs.

I'd never done ploughing. Ridging up potatoes was the extent of my experience, for that we used a double breasted plough, to lift the earth around the plants.

My first lesson came out of the blue. I was busy at stone carting. There were plenty of stones in the fields at Glympton for we were on the flank of the Cotswold Country. I'd been busy picking and carting stones for a week and I was sick of stones. Mid-afternoon the carter came into the field, he hadn't a lot of time but no doubt wanted to strike his first 'land' out, ready for a good start come morning.

Already the afternoon sun was entangled in the branches of the elms, running down the sky as if he would cool his feet in the round pond. His rays caught the gleaming breast of the plough as the carter swung it round on the headland. That's a man-sized job I thought as I watched the carter striding up the field, setting his markers up and pacing the land out.

I had a load almost ready to empty at the woodside and I went close as I dared to try to catch his eye. Carter, intent upon the job in hand, took no notice. I tipped the load. Already he had his first ridge set up — two furrows facing each other, ready for him to plough up one side and down the other.

A great bull voice hailed me, 'Young David.'

'Yes,' I answered, eagerness in my voice.

'Wanna plough?'

'Oh yes, Carter,' I could hardly believe my luck.

'Well doan'ee stand there gawpin'. Grab 'old of the 'andles an' listen.'

I did so and felt with a shock the dead inert weight of the plough.

'Look up the field lad.' His great hand was tight on my shoulder. 'See yon rag in the ash under the wood?'

'Aye,' I nodded.

'Well, that be me marker. Keep yer eyes on that and mind, dunna look back. Go on, 'aven't got much day left.'

'Get up,' I chirruped. The great horses never so much as twitched an ear.

'Dammee, David. Speak to 'em hearty. They'll go,' yelled Carter impatiently.

I took a deep breath. 'Get up.' Whew! the plough shot forward, I nearly let go of the handles in my unreadiness and we were off. I could feel the velvet mouths through the long lines in my hands and gripped the plough handles. It was the most exhilarating feeling I have ever known. The plough slid along, lissom and manoeuvrable. I was ploughing and suddenly added five feet to my rather inadequate five feet four and a bit. It was really quite easy and, proud as a peacock, I turned to see where I'd been. We hit a big stone in that split second and all hell was let

loose. The plough kept going, bucking and rearing like a
wild creature. A handle whipped out of my hand and
caught me under the ribs. I gasped, 'I can't do it.' Two
hands came round and clamped mine back on the handles.

'No, an' yer never will if yer keep looking back. Look
up. Look to the end of the field lad an' plough.'

Carter had been behind me every step of the way.

3. *The Wheel Mark*

We were drilling barley, a pair of horses hitched to the
drill. Horses that would show any tractor a thing or two
— at least that's what the waggoner reckoned.

They stood on that October morning, proud in their
gleaming harness, patiently waiting whilst we teemed the
seed corn into the drill. Molly and Dolly, their sleek coats
shining with half-crowns, the fruit of much hard grooming.

A robin sang from the holly bush, corn spilled over the
side of the drill. 'Dangee, boy! Stop a'listening to that fool
bird and watch what yer doing!' The waggoner went on,
'I'll drill the headland. Reckon four rounds will do it. Allus
remember boy, leave a wide headland to turn round in,
then yer not for ever tramplin' on yer work.'

He set off following the hedge round the field, walking
behind the drill, guiding the team with the long reins. It
was a good-sized field and bait time had arrived by the
time he had finished the headland.

We sat under the hedge. Cold tea, bread and cheese and
an onion was our fare. As we ate, the horses stood noses to
hedge nipping off the hawthorn shoots.

Bait over we refilled the drill again and moved to the
mark, drilling now back and forth across the field. 'Right!'
said the waggoner. 'You can drill, 'tis time ye larnt. I'll go
over and fetch Captain and harrow in behind you.'

I stood with the reins in my hands, hesitating. 'But I. . .'
The waggoner shook with laughter, sending a wood pigeon
crashing away through the wood in panic.

'All right, I'll watch yer do a bout. Give you a start like.
Remember keep yer wheel about a foot inside yer mark.'

With far more confidence than I felt I spoke to the team. 'Git up Molly, Dolly.' We were off. The ground was dry and the tilth fine; it was hardly possible to see the mark I was following, let alone to keep a foot inside it with the wheel of the drill. I kept staring at the wheel in front of me, pulling first this rein, then that rein. Now I could see the mark — now I couldn't. The drill was weaving all over the place.

'Whoa,' shouted the waggoner. 'Yer'll have all the hares in creation breaking the legs down those rows!'

He beckoned. 'Leave the team and come here.' I dropped the reins and joined him. 'Now stand on the mark here and look up the field.' The line ran up the field as clear as a chalk mark on a blackboard.

'But I couldn't see it behind the drill. . .'

'No!' he broke in. 'You were too busy watching the wheel — or your feet! In a dry time the line is broken, but if yer take a long look, yer eyes pick up the wheel marks, then it's easy and yer'll drill straight.'

I must have looked a bit down in the mouth for he suddenly grinned at me. 'Don't fret. I know yer trying 'ard but that's yer trouble. Yer tryin' too 'ard. Larn ter relax like, walk easy an' enjoy the job, an' ye'll do all right.'

4. Hercules

The weeks slipped by and I was beginning to settle down into the quiet rhythm of country life. The days were long and good. More and more of my time was spent with the horses and I looked after four at Bell Farm. Three were no trouble — Dolly, Molly and Prince. True, Dolly loathed drawing a load downhill and would sit back in the britching and slither her back feet; Molly had a habit of dropping off to sleep in the shafts; Prince had the endearing habit of trying to take a bit out of the unwary hand that reached for his bridle to lead him, but by and large I could cope. The villain of the piece was Hercules.

He stood over seventeen hands, a great grey dappled Percheron gelding, a mountain of muscle and beauty with feet like soup plates. Every morning became a trial of strength or rather a battle of wills, between Hercules and myself, but Monday morning was the end. He would come out of the stable trembling with pent-up energy, bucking and rearing up onto his hindlegs, snorting and pawing the air with iron-shod hooves. Time and again I was lifted clean off the ground. I felt as helpless as a sheaf slipping into the steel maw of the threshing drum.

On this particular Monday I had orders to take the harrows and go to Long Heath where we were ploughing in Winter wheat. I took Dolly in the cart with a load of seed wheat and the harrows. Hercules was tied behind.

'Give him a day's harrowing, Davey,' said the waggoner. 'That should cool his ardour.'

It was easier said than done. I began to realise that everyone in the past had avoided working with the great mad horse; Hercules knew it and had gradually grown right out of control.

Long Heath reached, I handed Dolly and the cart over to the drill team and eventually got Hercules hitched to the harrows. I took the reins and without a word from me, he literally took off. The first turn up the field nearly killed me, the great horse all but galloped, the harrow leapt and skittered over the rough ploughing. My arms felt as though they would be pulled out of their sockets and twice I landed awkwardly twisting my ankles. The hedge at the far end of the field stopped Hercules and still snorting and trembling he stood, blowing clouds of vapour into the frosty air.

My mind was made up in that moment. Gathering the reins I hooked them over the hames of his collar, then turning him alongside the hedge, I quickly mounted him and sat side-saddle gripping the pointed hames. 'Go on then,' I yelled and away we went. I hardly remember the first time round that field. I was too busy hanging on for dear life. The second round was noticeably slower. I remember clearly the men on the drill staring open-mouthed at our mad progress. The third round of that fourteen acre field was almost at walking pace and Hercules was glad to stop when I called 'Whoa there!'

Straight away I turned into the work and took up my proper place with the long reins behind the shining harrows. 'Git up Hercules,' I shouted and we moved off. All that day, he worked as sweet as a nut. The waggoner came and watched our royal progress up the black furrows of plough. 'He be proper meek now,' said the old man, scratching his head in wonderment. I wondered at his use of the word 'meek' until one night I stumbled upon a saying of the ancient Greeks. 'He that is meek is a king among men!' The old waggoner was right. Hercules had become a king among horses — disciplined, self-controlled and obedient to the word of command.

5. *Bean Field*

One time Taffy said 'Go and harrow the Lizard.' He tore off in his Ford Prefect. I took a set of light harrows and Dolly. When I got to the gate, I stopped short. Taffy must have made a mistake. The Lizard was full of bean plants, they must have been over six inches high. 'It'll smash them to bits,' I mused. Half an hour passed, with me still hopping between two branches, whether to go back or get on with the harrowing.

A car screeched to a halt. 'What the hell are you looking at boy?'

'But the beans. . .' I stammered.

Dolly went on impassively chewing the hedge.

'What do you think they are, pineapples?' he raved. 'Git on and harrow them.' Still raving and with a tearing of gears that boded no good for the long life of his car, he shot away.

I harrowed them, flattened them, bruised and tore those bean plants, thinking that Taffy was a bit round the bend. Later that season, we had a tremendous thunderstorm. The following morning, on my way to Heath Farm, I passed the Lizard. The beans were standing proud, like ranks of soldiers. I went into the field to look at them. Nearly every plant had three stems. Taffy's voice boomed across from the lane. 'Try pulling one up, David.' I did, but I couldn't shift the plant.

'Beat 'em when they're young, boy. Makes 'em put their roots right down, then they stand the great storms like last night.' A gear-box's scream of agony and he was gone.

I worked a lot with the horses. There was a new waggoner, Reg Sircombe, he had come up from Mr. Good's property at Lusley in Devon. Reg had brought three pairs of Suffolk Punches with him. These were magnificent chestnuts with clean legs, as opposed to Shires that carry a lot of feather or hair around the feet. Suffolks were in their element, working Oxfordshire clay. The much-vaunted tractors were often bogged down in the sticky mud and did great damage with their enormous spinning wheels, whereas horses could pull anything. I doubt whether we would have got the mangolds and sugar beet off at all without the horses.

One tea-time I got back to Bell farm with my two horses. I'd been harrowing-in Winter wheat and was very tired. The method was this: once potatoes were lifted and the haulms or tops were cleared off, the ground was very clean and easy to work. The corn was drilled, then ploughed in and I followed after with the heavy harrows, or drags as they were often called. When I came to an open furrow, which occurred between two lands or strips of ploughing, I had to broadcast the seed by hand. I loved the job. I would set the horses facing down the furrow, take a hat full of corn and walk in front of them. The horses would follow without any bother and draw a straight line into the bargain. Heavy harrowing with a good steady team was hard on the ankles but very satisfying.

When I had returned and stabled the horses, I heard a terrific racket coming from the stackyard. It sounded like someone turning round and round on a tractor. Somewhat bemused I went out to see. There was Reg Sircombe, racing round on a brand new Ferguson tractor. He stopped when he saw me and patting the machine, said 'There you are middear. Ye can keep they horses o' mine from now on. This is where the overtime will be.' And I did, becoming under-waggoner with Big Bill, a great tree of a man from Berkshire. Bill wouldn't be seen dead on a tractor. 'Osses' were his life and he finished his working life with them.

I didn't blame Reg. He'd got a family to keep and that was all that mattered to him. Anyway I could see his point, a tractor didn't need feeding, grooming and cleaning down. At the end of the day you just switched off or at most filled up with T.V.O. to be ready for morning.

I loved working with the horses. I'd a lot to learn but there was plenty of time.

6. 'Tater Pickin''

By the time the women from the village arrived at the field to begin picking, the tractor driver had spun the first row of potatoes out. The machine was simple enough, a rotating wheel which carried a series of two tine claws, which in turn scooped the raised rows of plants up and scattered them, dropping the potatoes behind. A strong wire shield projected out on a long arm to ensure that the potatoes and stones did not fly too far but dropped in a fairly narrow band. The farm van often made two or three journeys to collect the women from the different points, sometimes travelling to the next village for pickers.

One of the older farm men, old John Ashby, acted as foreman in charge of the women. He needed to be a man of experience, firmness and tact, for the women were no fools at the game and knew all the tricks of the trade.

This particular morning I was in charge of the three horses and carts with two young teenagers, John and Bill. Our job was to empty the basket skeps as the women filled them, into the carts. As a cart was filled one of us would take the full load down to where the men were building the potato clamp or pie.

There were twenty pickers on this occasion and the foreman began to pace the row and mark each stint with a stick. Long Heath, the potato field, was almost twenty chains or cricket pitches in length. Maggie May, the sharp-tongued spokeswoman for all the pickers, walked with him, to ensure that all the stints were equal. The women then donned their aprons of sacking and moved to their places. In the dim misty light of that October morning, the women at the far end of the row were lost to sight.

The pickers at the beginning of the row had almost finished before the top women had reached their stint and the spinner started off again on the second row. The women picked rapidly and cleanly, straight into their sacking aprons which they held before them. 'Bottoms up' yelled Billy, with misguided cheekiness and then yelled again as a potato, aimed with deadly accuracy by Maggie, caught him on the side of the head. 'Mind yer manners, cheeky young devil' she spat out.

I was kept busy with the boys emptying the skeps into the carts and woe betide us if we kept any of the women waiting with an apronful of potatoes for an empty skep. Maggie had her own way of showing her disapproval. She would wait on such occasions until I had reached her with the needed skep and then 'accidentally' let her apron slip, tipping a heap of potatoes upon the ground. 'Na look at that,' she would cackle, shaking her head and turning away to continue picking. If the pace grew too fierce for the women a group of them would remove their aprons and depart into Long Heath Wood. 'Hey up!' John Ashby would shout. 'Taint bait time yet.'

'I'der know that,' Maggie would yell defiantly. 'Time fer a pee, even in harvest time!'

In the long run it paid the tractor driver to maintain a steady rhythm so that the women had time to straighten their backs as they walked back to the beginning of their stint and if they were lucky, a moment to squat on an upturned basket.

Two men worked down at the clamp, Harry Durrant was given the responsibility of choosing the site. Several factors had to be taken into consideration. The clamp had to be reasonably close to a hard road and the site must be dry and well drained and well away from dripping trees. It had also to be sheltered from the prevailing winds. As a rule Durrant used a North to South line, looking for the side protection of a wood or high bank to the East, for when Winter comes it is no fun riddling and bagging up potatoes in a bitter wind. Each cartload had to be shaped as it was tipped, the man using wide, many tined, potato forks to build the high sloping sides. Batons of straw were laid down to mark the width of the clamp until the potatoes were settled and then more batons were laid on like thatch to make a frost-proof roof. The batons were held in place temporarily by spadefuls of earth, until there was time to cover the whole clamp with soil. Once the site had been chosen, the plough was run round several times, so that there was no shortage of easily available soil for the builders.

After a week of picking I was asked to drive the spinner, the tractor driver being needed elsewhere on the farm. It made a pleasant change, emptying potato skeps all day was a tiring business. I soon learnt how to adjust the blade of the spinner, so that I wasn't guilty of slicing the potatoes, before spinning them out, and realised for the first time how quickly the spinner could become clagged up with haulms that had not yet rotted.

Old John Ashby went missing with a bout of lumbago and I found myself acting as foreman for the pickers. They really had a field day and Maggie ran rings around me. When I paced the rows out she insisted that I had made a mistake, and each time she disagreed with me I conscientiously retraced my steps and paced the row again. I soon realised that they were just playing me up, the more time I messed about measuring the stints the less time they had to spend bending their backs to pick. They were paid by the day and it was no loss to them.

Normally the setting of the stints only happened once a day, depending upon the number of pickers, but few fields are regular in shape and Long Heath was no exception. At the far end the boundary fence cut back and followed the wood at a very sharp angle. This meant that the rows became noticeably shorter with each successive row. The woman picking the top stint didn't mind but Maggie did, within minutes all the women were round my tractor like a swarm of angry bees. 'If I'm ter pick a chain, then she be,' screeched Maggie, above the noise of the tractor. 'An ye can turn that yammering critter off. We ainer pickin' no more you, till stints be straight!'

I clambered down, longing for the presence of John Ashby. 'I'll go and have a look,' I said. 'Ye'll need to do more than look,' rejoined Maggie tartly. I walked off up the field, glad to get away from the sharp voices. The afternoon was almost spent and the mist was thickening again.

It was then that I realised that the short rows or pikes, as we called them, ran out at the end of the Long Heath wood. Once we reached that point the rows would finish level with the bottom boundary of the wood and all would be well. I took a line across the rows and cut off, as it were, the offending stints. Then I walked down the row dividing it into nineteen. I knew now what I was going to do and I turned to walk back to tell the women, but where were they? All I could see was the dark earth vanishing into a wall of swirling mist. I shouted into the nothingness and a chorus of voices answered me somewhere to my left. I could just make out the words 'We're a comin'. Don't fret yerself.' Then as the mist cleared momentarily I saw them and went no nearer. The women stood in a circle, facing outwards, their aprons spread to form a curtain of sacking. They looked like a gathering of witches on some blasted heath rather than a concession to modesty as some of their number obeyed the call of nature.

Soon they were gathered around me and before Maggie had time to start, I pitched in. 'I've measured the rows level with the wood end. Nineteen stints and they're all the same distance and a bit shorter than before. I turned to a good-looking, dark-haired young woman, 'Margaret, you've been picking the top stint haven't you?' She nodded. 'Well, your stint will be a bit longer than the others now, but it will get gradually shorter, until we reach the woodside and then you will all start on equal terms again.' Margaret nodded agreement, she was quick-witted enough to see that in the long run, she would come off best.

Maggie led the women back to the row, satisfied that I had been put in my place, and peace was restored.

It was no accident that Margaret happened to be at the

top of the field. I knew that Maggie had put her there with strict instructions to waste as much of the tractor driver's time as possible, by engaging him in pleasant conversation. The longer she talked the more rest the women had between rows. I knew that it was the same at the other end of the field and in my first days had fallen into the trap many times until the Manager put me wise.

Knocking off time came none too soon and I watched the women fill their aprons with potatoes for the last time that day. These were their 'puddings' which they were allowed to take home as a bonus each day. I watched them because they had got into the habit of taking carrier bags with them onto the field and filling them as well. We had even caught them packing potatoes into their lunch tins. It had become too much of a good thing. Twenty pickers could walk off with a lot of potatoes, in any case a picker with her concession of a daily pudding could build up a stock of potatoes to keep her family throught the Winter.

7. *End of the Day*

When I had a team of horses out on really heavy work such as ploughing or carting off sugar beet from wet sticky land, we loosed out at three-thirty and made for home. It has to be remembered that the field we were working in might be as much as three miles from the stables. At the end of the working day we never rode the horses home, they had had enough by then. Head down, lathered with sweat and muck they plodded along, the beautiful feathered feet of the Shires, heavy and clagged with mud.

We, the waggoners, walked alongside, tired yet content, with the knowledge of a good day's work behind us. Blue smoke curled from our small black pipes with their bent stems. One learnt very quickly that a straight-stemmed pipe had a short life. They would snap like dried twigs in the pocket, as one bent about the work. I lost several pipes, when carelessly jumping onto my charge's back, to ride to the work field in the morning. Thermos flasks were avoided for the same reason, we carried sweet cold milkless tea in bottles. Later I learnt to keep my tea fairly warm by placing the bottle in the horse's nosebag which was filled with crushed oats and chaff sweetened with molasses. Our bait bags were slung with the nosebag over the shining brass hames, which fitted snugly around the horse collar. Hames were not there to be ornamental, like all farm gear they were both beautiful and functional, they carried the strong hooks over which to slip the pulling tugs, to harness the tremendous power of the great horses.

As soon as the horses were unhitched from the carts, we led them straight into their stalls. We liked them to cool off before slaking their thirst at the water trough. Off came the pad and britching harness, then bridle and great collar, before the stall bridle was put on. This was secured to the stall by a rope which, passing through an iron ring on the manger, was tied to a large free-running bobbin or plug of wood. In this way the horse was given freedom of movement to pull at the hay in the rack above the stall, to feed from the manger or to lie down. We gave them a feed of crushed oats, wheat chaff and molasses and set to work grooming them. When the horses were wet from rain or sweat-lathered, they were brushed down with a figure of eight made from straw, this also helped to get the circulation going and warmed them up. The next job was to wash their 'feathers' and feet. I always enjoyed combing the long silky hairs or feathers of the Shire horses. The brown and gold Suffolk Punches, of which I had three, had very clean legs and no feather, they were much easier to manage, but I always thrilled to the sight of Shires moving in full harness, majestic was the word for them. The extra work entailed was well worth it.

Finally I used the curry comb for any caked mud which brushing had failed to shift, then rough brushed them all over including mane and tail, finishing off with the smooth dandy brush. I loved to see the coats shine up as I dandied them, making the 'half crowns come', the old waggoners used to call it, the dapplings of sunlight upon a sleek healthy coat.

In Spring and Summer the horses lay outside; we would put halters on them and lead them across the road to their pasture. I can see it now, the field gate swinging slowly open, then halters off, and away Molly and Dolly, Prince and Captain would go. Frisking and bucking, tearing round the field like enormous mad March hares, as if they had never known what work was. There was something strangely endearing in the sight of those great giants, fat bodies prone, legs waving madly skyward, wriggling and squirming from side to side, then up on their feet to give a thunderous shake from head to tail, then back to tranquil, grazing sanity.

A new bailiff arrived. Taffy had more than enough to cope with, with his own acres. Mr. Brown held a Degree in Agriculture. A week later a brand-new Fisher Humphrey three-furrow plough arrived. 'Bring her into the barn, Charlie,' said the bailiff. 'We'll get her levelled up, ready for you to plough Holly Bush.'

Charlie said nothing, though the snort he emitted was eloquent enough. The plough was brought onto the concrete floor of the great barn. Steel rule and spirit level were produced. 'Nothing like doing the job properly,' said Mr. Brown briskly. Eventually the job was done and correct in every detail. Charlie went forth to plough. Without a word he set into the work and pulled away. The result was hopeless, one furrow too deep, one furrow too shallow, nor did the plough seem to be pulling straight. Mr. Brown's face was a picture, the old hands watching, feasted upon it. Charlie swung round in his tractor seat and heaved himself out and down. On the ground he was a caricature of a man. He didn't walk, he waddled; two smashed hips from the Dardanelles saw to that. As he waddled his bottom stuck out a mile and his great bald head swayed from side to side. On the quiet the children called him Humpty Dumpty but with no malice in their voices.

'Give me a bloody spanner,' he rasped. An adjustment here, a sharp tap there, and he was in the seat again. He pulled forward, then down again he came, to hit an offending part with his hammer. Then away again. The plough was ploughing like a dream. You could put a level over the three furrows. Charlie swung round in his seat and yelled. The wind took his words but we heard all right. 'Ye can keep yer fairy book farming.' Charlie was king that day.

8. *Summertime*

When Summer came it was one to remember, almost sixteen weeks of sunshine. I scythed round my last field of corn that harvest. It was Will's Grave near the crossroads. Will had been hanged nearby in Gallows Furlong years back in the 18th century for sheep-stealing. They reckoned that the wood for this gibbet came from the next field, 'Poles Furlong'. I always enjoyed using a scythe and corn cutting was wonderfully satisfying. To hear the blade, biting into the standing corn and the swishing rustle as it fell took some beating. Behind me a lad tied the corn into sheaves. All around us while we worked were the sights and sounds and scents of Summer. The flapping tongues of poppy flame, blue scabious, tiny scarlet pimpernel and pink corn-cockles, Dog daisies and the purple vetch. A rabbit popping its head out of the corn, and sometimes a deer, head above the corn as if swimming in a golden sea. Close upon our heels came the binder and thanks to the path we had cut, the horses had a clear passage and no corn was trampled and wasted.

Stooking began as soon as four rows of sheaves were laid and by the time the corn still to be cut stood like a rapidly shrinking island in the midst of the serried ranks of fallen sheaves, perhaps twenty men would be busy stooking — setting the sheaves to stand in the words of Victoria Sackville-West, which 'like a tented army dreams away the night, beneath the moon in silvered fields.'

As the island of corn shrank, strange movements could be seen, the panic rushes of animals that had stayed overlong in their familiar refuge. Work would stop, apart from the clacking knife and flashing arms of the binder, and we would gather for the kill. Chasing the fleeing rabbits, as they lolloped over the sheaves, and there were dinners for all by the time we had stopped wielding our sticks.

143

9. *Country Characters*

Harvest time was one of the few times during the year when all the farm workers came together. They were great days, the hours were long and the work hard but one got a deep sense of fulfilment and satisfaction. Odd moments stand out in the memory and defy the passing seasons. The night we loaded the last waggon of barley sheaves in Barn Ground, the dry stubble still crackling under our weary feet and a great harvest moon sailing above the elm trees. Pikes on our shoulders, their prongs quicksilver in moonlight, we followed the load through the open gate. Alfie swung it shut and as it clashed into the catch, metal on metal, Old Ben began to sing 'Come Ye Thankful People Come'. We sang the load home, the harvest was over and we were glad.

Alfie was always getting his leg pulled, in some ways he never grew up, and yet no matter how the other men ragged him, Alfie never got riled. They never let him forget the time when mounted on a Fordson tractor, ploughing Will's Grave, he had driven straight through the hedge onto the wide roadside verge beyond, shouting 'Whoa! Whoa dammee!'

Machines were slowly but surely replacing the horses and Albert, who drove the massive caterpillar tractor D2, was regarded with grudging admiration by the older hands. He was thickset and swarthy, with a violent and unpredictable temper. Two terriers followed him like shadows much to the annoyance of the gamekeeper, for they arrived each morning to work with Albert, sitting like statues upon the petrol tank of his motorbike. No-one argued with him, though we cursed the efficiency of those terriers when we waited for the rabbits bolting in panic from the hungry binder at harvest time.

Archie was often with us. He had a curious way of raising his hand as he stammered, bringing it down with a resounding thwack onto his knee as the desired word came charging forth. Archie was second rick builder when Durrant couldn't be on the rick. It might happen that we were topping out a rick — finishing the roof — and then

Archie would take on the new rick and start setting the bottom out.

As we lazed at mealtimes on couches of sheaves from nearby stooks the older men delighted in pulling Archie's leg. 'That far side's going out a bit Archie.' And Archie would have to go and look to reassure himself. 'Reckon ye'll need a couple of "policemen" fer that 'un Archie.' 'Policemen' were long wooden props which were thrust into the side of the rick when it looked unsafe. They stayed there until the rick settled down. There would be a choking noise as Archie spluttered his rage into the bottle of cold tea poised at his lips and a great roar of mirth from the tormentors. George Blackwell had the name of 'Blackie'. I regarded him with something approaching awe, though often his fellow workers called him a durned fool. He had an amazing capacity for work. I'd see him leaving the farmyard with a horse and cart, his chin thrust out, puffing and blowing as he muttered to himself, walking by his horse with quick jerky steps, looking for all the world like a spinach-filled 'Popeye' bent upon an urgent mission, with the sands of time running out. Blackie would set his cart against the hayrick and then proceed to cut the hay, pitch it down onto the waggon and then load it, before climbing up onto the rick again to cut more hay. I've seen him jumping up and down like an irate staghound, all the while keeping up an apparently ceaseless diatribe against the injustice of sending a man on his own. Then down Blackie would jump for the last time, sling a rope over to steady the load and off back to the farm to unload. Blackie perhaps enjoyed being put upon, for he never once complained to the bailiff and I've seen him go back for a second load in the same morning.

Whenever I think of Bell Farm and Oxfordshire, George Pilgrim comes into my mind. I didn't realise it then, but he was the pattern of farmworkers to come. In those days he was something of a rarity on the farm, a mechanic to his fingertips. Charlie, 'Humpty Dumpty', went by rule of thumb, a deep instinct born of his knowledge of the fields in which he had worked for many years. He knew where the patches of stone were, the bands of clay, the ground

145

that would always lie wet, and worked accordingly. George Pilgrim was different, he worked by the blueprint and hard-won first-hand experience of the increasing number of new and complex machines. He was quiet, lightly built yet as strong and springy as true steel. George loved machinery and all his spare time was spent pottering around the latest machinery and gadgets on other farms in the district. Anything new from milking machines to combines and corn driers drew him like a magnet. At showtime he well-nigh made his bed in the machinery section.

George Pilgrim was popular because so often he helped us out of a sticky corner and gave us the chance to get on with the job. Yet he never threw his knowledge at us or paraded it. 'Send for George Pilgrim' was a familiar cry and the farmworker of tomorrow was already there, his foot firmly in the farming door.

10. *The Monsters*

Over at Enstone, Taffy Hughes, our former manager, ran a lot of barley land. The year of the long summer we went from Glympton to help with the harvest. I remember sitting with the other men as we ate our bait, watching three great yellow monsters each towed by a tractor, eating their way around the whitening barley acres. No cutting round now with a scythe, straight in they went. 'Bloody waste' spat Fred. 'They just flatten the first cut. They'll never pick all that corn up. Barley's dead ripe — t'old heads jest snap off.'

'Yer jest an' ole hoss man talkin' you!' laughed 'Sniffer' — so called because his nose was permanently adorned with a dewdrop. 'Doan 'ee mock I,' snapped Fred. 'Iva bin a hoss man since I leff school. An' I be most proud of it but mark this Sniffer, I was allus master of my osses. Taint so wi' them,' he pointed his stubby black pipe at one of the offending combines humming past in a cloud of dust. His voice rose to a shout above the clamour 'They be the bosses na. We mun kip pace wi' them an' they buggers doan' git tired like we!'

One of the men spoke, 'Doan' ee fret Fred. Reckon a few years from now, they'll be stoppin' 'oles in the 'edges wi' yon tin creations.'

Rolf got to his feet and blinked his one red-rimmed rheumy eye and remarked sagely, 'Well, I'm thinkin they's come to stay you. 'Tis only the beginnin' '.

Alfie chimed in 'Aye, osses are on the way out an' I reckon us men'll foller.'

It was a prophetic word. Long before that first day ended I had also realised the truth of Fred's words. The combines had left the field by tea-time and we were left with the Herculean task of dragging the sacks of corn into great heaps with sack burrows. The machines had out-paced us, we were just not geared to cope with such a prodigious output of work.

Anyone who has walked a Cotswold field will know that there is more flint than earth. Pulling the laden sack barrow downhill was child's play but pulling it on the level or, much worse, uphill, was killing work. It took two men, one straining at the handles and the second pushing with all his might. Every sack had to be safely under the tarpaulins by nightfall, and we tugged and pulled our insides out long after dark had come, slipping and sliding on the loose flints, cursing the labour-saving devices of the machine age.

If there were any rabbits in that first memorable combine harvest field we didn't see them. Old Rolf said he reckoned they'd all died of fright. Perhaps the fact that the havesters cut the stubble very high up, meant that the cutter bar went clean over the top of the squatting rabbits.

The next morning we went back to the harvest field with its black tarpaulin covered heaps of corn. It seemed a far cry from the days of the harvest hymn:
'Every youth and maiden
On the harvest plain
Round the waggons laden
With the golden grain.'

Our gang was small, two tractor drivers with their trailers and two loaders. The first load wasn't too bad. One man loaded his trailer whilst Fred and I lifted the sacks of corn up to him. The fourth man stood behind us and gave the sack a push at the crucial point and took the full weight from us.

Fred and I used a lifting stick, we each seized the sack by the scruff of the neck with one hand and the stick man holding the lifting stick with left hand passed it behind the sack to his partner. The sack was then pulled smartly back against the stick which formed the fulcrum and in the same moment we would lift together. Perfect timing and co-ordination was vital, otherwise the whole weight of two hundred weight could fall upon one lifter. The fourth man was a tremendous help, for the early tractor trailers were not designed for this kind of work, they were far too high. This was made even more obvious by the fact that Fred and I were both small men, we didn't make eleven feet between us.

At last the first trailer load was on its way out of the field and we turned our attention to the second trailer. Without the fourth man it was killing work. Fred and I could manage to get the bottom of the sack we were lifting onto the edge of the trailer bed, but time and again we failed to get enough swing to push the sack up and over. We were just congratulating each other when Taffy Hughes arrived to ask why we had taken so long and that there was another sixteen acre field of barley strewn with sacks waiting to be stacked up against the coming night. 'Told ee young un,' said Fred with bitterness in his voice, 'Machines be master now.'

11. *Wintertime*

An icy wind screamed over the open ploughing. It was a 'lazy wind' as country folk say, not stopping to go round anything but cutting straight through. Breathing out of doors made the lungs ache and one's face and hands soon lost all feeling but numbness. The great bullfinch hedges were bowed down under the weight of snow and until the lanes were cleared of drifts our only means of transport was the shepherd's float. I led Jorrocks, the faithful cob, along the tops of the hedges in order to reach stock with hay and corn. The fun began when I reached a gateway and the hedge ended abruptly and Jorrocks and I would be floundering in deep snow, up to my shoulders, until our feet could find purchase again upon the next length of hedgerow.

The snow and hard frosts continued and we began to use new routes across the iron-hard ploughlands. Here the driving winds gave the snow no chance to settle but swept it with scant ceremony into the lanes already choked with great drifts.

Within a stone's throw of Bell Farm a pair of barn owls moved up and down the thick tussock rows of cocksfoot grass. All day long they kept unwearying vigil, they were too hungry to care about mere men. Birds died in their hundreds, many of them frozen to death as they roosted and fell asleep for the last time. A peregrine sat on the telegraph pole at Will's Grave. I saw him there for a week or more, he looked at home in the white waste, as cruel and merciless as the weather. I suppose he was only struggling for survival like everything else.

Rabbits and hares came into the cottage gardens and made new homes beneath the snow-buried patches of cabbage and brussels sprouts. Once in the yellow light of late afternoon I heard the shrill voices of fitches (stoats and weasels) coming towards me as I made my way homeward from Long Heath. The concrete roadway up to the rickyard had been cleared of snow. I climbed a five-bar gate and watched them pass, there must have been twenty, lithe, sinuous killers with needle sharp teeth, yikkering to each other as they hastened to the feasts of fat mice and rats in Long Heath ricks.

As soon as possible Old Nodder and I got the flock out onto a windswept stretch of road and gave them a good run. Each day they were released from the fold and given this exercise. Standing about in a narrow pen was no good to ewes heavily in lamb, they would soon be off their feet altogether.

Spring was late that year but it came as always with the shouting of birds in the deep woods and the black snow water turning the quiet River Glym into a watery broom

wielded by some frenzied giant to sweep the rubbish of
Winter out of the valley. The deep lane which led to the
thatched peace of Crow Barn grew green overnight with
dog's-mercury and bluebell stars. Wych elms glowed red
with breaking flowers in the welcome sun and beyond the
golden sleet of hazel catkins the alder buds wore purple
gloves for Easter's coming and hung their brown catkins
above the racing river.

12. *New Pastures*

I was growing restless, feeling the need for new experi-
ences. I applied for an ex-serviceman's course in Agriculture
and was given a place. The course didn't start until the following September and I decided to spend the intervening
months working at a dairy farm back at Northchurch. I
knew that I would miss the countryside of Oxfordshire,
the sunken lanes that wound through wooded valleys and
the long narrow ribbons of upland road, bounded on either
side by the great wide verges. These were my delight, a
no-man's land, the kingdom of the long acre. Nature's own
herbaceous border alight with flowers in their season, the
serried ranks of stately foxgloves, clumps of cowslip, grown
tall in the long grass, red campions which seemed to glow
from amongst the brambles of the hedgeback and, perhaps
most beautiful of all, the purple mounds of meadow cranes-
bill. This was a paradise for many butterflies and I never
tired of watching them as I rode the great horses side-saddle
to work in the fields. The scourge of the chemical spray
was still a few years away and the roadman's scythe and
sickle was no enemy but held a true economy within its
curving blade. Marbled-whites and Common Blues, like bits
of truant sky, held court here. Often I saw Purple Hair-
streaks upon the bramble flowers, Peacocks flirted their
wings and showed bright eyes upon the purple beds of
creeping thistle. Painted Lady and Clouded Yellow —
summer migrants — came to English country lanes and
brought their beauty to the ever-changing mosaic,
flowers winged and rooted.

I had grown to love Oxford, too. Often I would walk the twelve miles from Glympton and spend all Saturday browsing round the bookshops. Books were friends and nobody seemed to mind if I spent all afternoon reading in an upstairs window seat, my only timekeeper being the College clocks. It seems to have become the fashion to sneer at poets like Matthew Arnold, Adam Lindsay Gordon, and William Morris, but I loved them and owe much to them. Edward Thomas, Robert Frost and T.S. Eliot opened up new worlds of perception and now and again I emptied my pockets and clutching my precious haul, walked home again, having spent even my bus fare. My bookshelf grew too small and Edgar would greet my arrival home with 'I dunno, reckon ye'll need a waggon ter git moved Davey. Can't be doing yer 'ead much though, all this readin' lark!'

One morning in April I packed my kit and left Glympton. Before breakfast that day I had walked up the valley for the last time and sat for a while on a knoll above the footbridge. It was a place where Keats's 'Sleep and Poetry' could have been written. I saw a dog stoat cross the bridge and heard a rabbit scream as the stoat killed at the edge of the spinney, then I heard him yikker and his mate ran across the bridge to him, followed closely by a line of three bounding youngsters. They, too, were busy learning the arts of living.

INTERLUDE

1. *Jerseys Galore*

I was cycling to work, it had just gone 4.30 a.m. by the Church clock. I was back in Northchurch and I felt at home. The village street was deserted and still and the air had that golden unused look about it. It was Maytime and the morning tide of birdsong washed over me. Every gatepost had become a rostrum for a songbird, there weren't enough gateposts to go round, nor enough branches to perch on. No matter, songthrushes, blackbirds and robins just sat in the roadway and sang. I cycled round them.

I had started milking in the New Shed. Here were the thirty heaviest milkers in the herd of 200 and they were milked three times a day. At 5.00 a.m., 2.00 p.m. and 9.00 p.m. We did little else but milk, using machines, of course. When we had finished milking a cow, the unit was weighed, the yield recorded and the milk emptied into a churn. When the churn was full I switched the filter head on to a new churn and wheeled the full one down to the dairy. Here the dairy maids took over, cooling, straining again and then bottling the milk.

Though the hours were long we had more time off during the day. One hour for breakfast and two hours for dinner, plenty of time to relax and read. The herdsman in charge of New Shed was a dour Scotsman, known to all as Mac. He was first-class at his job and never told me to do anything without giving the reason. I'd always thought that the one reason for washing a cow's udder before milking, was the obvious one of cleanliness. Mac taught me that it was this and something more.

'Change your water regular. No use washing a cow wi' pea soup. Keep it hand warm and wash the whole bag. Not a lick and a promise.'

At first my job was just this, washing the cows, weighing and recording the milk, and giving the cows their ration of cake according to yield. Above each cow was a board giving her name, date of calving, last week's average daily yield and her daily ration of dairy cake. There was also room for her date of calving once she had been served by the bull and had held to him.

I became an expert cow washer and in my enthusiasm would get well ahead of Mac. Apart from this it gave me a break. One morning when I was blissfully streaking ahead, Mac stopped me.

'Come here, David.' Mac was standing beside the last cow I had attended to. 'Feel that udder,' he said. I did so, it was firm and full. 'You've washed four cows ahead of me. Go down the row and feel their udders.'

Obediently I went back to each one. 'Notice anything?' queried Mac.

'Yes, Mac. The bag's quite slack in the first two.'

Mac grinned. 'Ye see Laddie, washing tells the cow she's going to be milked and, more important to her, that she's going to be fed. The warm water stimulates the hormones, oxy-tocin they calls it, and she lets her milk down. But if she's not fed and the effect of your washing and rubbing has worn off, then she feels let down. Result — a drop in yield.

I learnt from this never to get too far in front of Mac, though this wasn't easy when four cows were milking at once.

Later I took two milking units and Mac two and we did our own washing, feeding and milking.

There were eight herdsmen, including the Head Herdsman. He never got his hands dirty. He would walk round the shed every morning in his tweed cap, Norfolk Jacket, riding breeches and polished leggings. He saw to the pedigree record side and was responsible for all the rations for each milker. Show preparation and calving came under him and his assistant, Reg.

Occasionally, when the Head Herdsman and Reg were away at shows or sales, Mac and I went in to milk the record holders. I never enjoyed this. These cows hardly ever went out. Two of them had held the world record for a Jersey, their udders were so large that they had difficulty in walking. We hand milked them into tiny calf buckets, it was impossible to get anything larger under them.

Mac called them 'Bloody slot machines — not like real cows at all. Put so many pounds of cake in and get so many gallons out.'

They were kept in special boxes but the very boxes smelt of dairy cake.

The months flew by and I was not sorry when September approached. The ordinary herdsmen, like myself, had nothing else to do but milk the cows and wash the sheds out. The money was good but the work routine became very monotonous and boring. I had grown used to being involved in each and every job on a farm, here in the super-efficient milk factory we rapidly became just cogs in the machine, with no real responsibility or say in the breeding programmes or rearing methods. The latter made me fume, the calves were reared in a hothouse atmosphere, which to my mind meant pampered, cossetted stock prone to every trouble going around and with very little built-in resistance to disease. I remembered the animal husbandry techniques used to such great effect by the writers of that fine book *The Farming Ladder*, the Henderson brothers of Oathill Farm in Oxfordshire. Healthier Jerseys it would have been difficult to find. I had often seen the farm whilst working at Glympton.

2. *Fairy Book Farming*

September came and I went for my year's Agricultural Training to Newton Hall near Cambridge. I suppose I did learn a certain amount about the theoretical side of farming, but much of it was superfluous repetition, as I had covered the ground for the most part already in my practical work during four and a half years as a farm worker. Many of the methods advocated, particularly in the field of crop husbandry, belonged to the sphere known as 'fairy book' farming. Animal Husbandry and Veterinary Hygiene were the bright spots in the course and I gained something of a grounding in genetics, nutrition and dairy hygiene. One subject left me with a life-long interest, beekeeping, and I shall always be grateful to David, the lecturer. His own deep love for bees made his lectures compelling and the infection was catching!

At the end of the year I answered an advertisement and got the post of assistant on a 300-acre farm in Galloway and I could not get there quickly enough.

GALLOWAY DAYS

1. *Mr. Jamieson*

The train from the South drew into Newton Stewart station. At last I would be meeting Mr. Jamieson. I suppose I was ready for anything. The long trip North had already stretched my mind from the green handkerchief fields of Oxfordshire with their guardian elms to the aching vastness of the wide moors. Glympton Park, the great house and rook-blessed church had given place to white-washed crofts set in misty valleys.

I staggered stiff-legged down onto the platform, thrown off balance by my bulging suitcase and army kitbag. There stood Mr. Jamieson. I had no doubt about that in my mind, it just could not be anyone else. He stood well over six foot, tweed-clad, deerstalker-crowned, dark piercing eyes and black walrus moustache, which hid a firm but generous mouth. He leant upon a wide-necked dalesman's crook, regarding me, his two sheep dogs at his feet: the phlegmatic Potter as black as coal and Moses, a dapper, tearaway dandy of a Border collie.

'You'll be David. Welcome to Galloway. I've got the car just outside.' A quick handshake and he turned and led the way.

Never a man of many words but a man, as I was to come to learn, of infinite resource, courage, dry humour, and sensitivity. If this seems too idyllic a picture, Mr. Jamieson had also a temper, violent and unpredictable as a Summer storm, but as brief.

One such occasion I shall never forget. I had been sent to plough one of the little fields near Ninian's Well, which stood on the old Edinburgh to Whitehorn road, now overgrown and unused for the most part, but open a carriage width at one end to give access to our farm and the two crofts above us. The field had been down to grass from time out of mind. Mr. Jamieson hoped to put it down to kale for Winter feeding for the Ayrshires.

161

I took the Ferguson and marked out the headland and the first land. The earth looked black and good, but I kept running into trouble halfway across the field. At first when the plough jumped out I thought I had found a boulder, but then I realised that the 'boulder' reached from dyke to dyke across the field. I had been ploughing out my first land for some while when Mr. Jamieson appeared and stood watching me. I reached the invisible dyke and up jumped the plough, clean out of the ground. I weighed on the hydraulic lever, struggling to get the plough back into the work but naturally it took several feet before I had reached my proper depth again. No sound from Mr. Jamieson. I turned at the top of the field and back into the furrow. The minute my share found the dyke up rose the plough and the struggle began again.

A great roar burst from the boss. 'You bloody clown get her down! Down! Down! Hell's bells and buckets of blood, you daft ninny! Get her down!'

Mr. Jamieson was jumping up and down like a pile-driver gone mad, great hands waving protest in the air. I turned in haste at the headland, saying nothing but thinking a lot, and away back up the field. The roar which greeted the plough as it rose like a shining Phoenix from the earth, had to be heard to be believed. 'No! No! Damn and set fire to the boy. You bloody clown! Get her down! Down!'

I stopped the tractor and jumped down. The Welsh in me was already boiling and popping in my chest, but I was still calm enough not to approach too near the apoplectic Mr. Jamieson.

'I'm no bloody clown,' I yelled at him. 'If you can do better, you're welcome.' I nodded towards the silent tractor and poised plough. 'She's all yours!' I walked back to the farm and set about getting a load of silage in from the pit, in readiness for the evening feed after milking.

Mr. Jamieson came back at tea-time. I heard the splutter of the Ferguson as he parked it. I awaited his entry into the milking byre with some apprehension. I was already milking when he loomed tall in the doorway. He looked over to me. 'Bit of a bugger that old dyke,' he said. A grin spread over his face and he turned away to go and fetch another milking unit. We neither of us referred to the incident again.

The other side to Mr. Jamieson's character came also as a shock, or rather a revelation. I had grown to regard him with great respect. A legacy from action in the first World War had meant years of pain and inaction. The prospect of his never walking again, had been accepted by all but himself. Now he walked and worked Cairn farm, still sleeping upon a board bed. Still forced to shear his sheep from a standing position. I used to tie the Blackface ewes in a corner of the 'fank' and put a sack over their heads, so that they would not struggle. Mr. Jamieson would shear them from front to back, lifting the fleece back over. As they had no belly wool, the method worked.

A rock of a man then but I was to be reminded that rocks hold other forms within themselves. I came into the kitchen one Saturday afternoon to find it empty, but lying on the table was an open book. I looked down and saw a flower. A yellow rock-rose from the moor. I went to pick it up and could not and never would. It was the most delicate painting I had ever seen, one plate of a collection Mr. Jamieson was busy working on each evening.

I thought of the fragile fronds of fossil fern hidden deep in the heart of the rocks which strew the hills around us. Just rocks to the casual eye, until split by circumstance when the inner beauty is revealed.

2. *Barney Hill*

I stood with Mr. Jamieson one clear morning on the top of Barney Hill. 'If we could reclaim this,' he said, swinging his crook round in a wide arc, we'd have nearly twenty acres of good grazing. What do you think about it?'

I looked at the forest of bracken, strewn with massive boulders. The Eastern side of the hill was steep, easily one in two, if not more in places.

'Well,' I said, choosing my words, 'the bracken is no real problem, we can smash that first with the heavy bar and harrows. The Ferguson plough will manage all right, but we'll have to plough the East face one way, and these boulders will cause some problems. What sort of soil depth can we reckon on?'

'I thought you'd raise that one,' laughed Mr. Jamieson. He pointed to one grey monster half-hidden by bracken. 'Come and look at this.'

We walked over to the rock. 'Put your hand over that rock and tell me what you feel,' he said.

'Why,' I exclaimed, 'it's almost smooth, and rounded, a sort of granular rock.'

'There's your answer,' said Mr. Jamieson. 'I reckon that Barney Hill is a heap of glacial debris. These rocks have been rolled and ground smooth. They'll be pigs to shift but the soil is good and deep.'

The conquest of Barney Hill took weeks of sweat and toil. A job not without its dangers, as we both found out. We took 'Chitta-bang', the old spike-wheeled Fordson up on to the hill, to pull the boulders out. Each one had to be dug around until enough rock was exposed to give the chain purchase when we slipped the loop over it. Then Mr. Jamieson or myself would mount the old war horse and draw the chain tight. Often the chain would fly forward like a bolt from a gun. This was not funny, especially when we were working on the steep face of the hill.

When the chain eventually got a good 'bite', the tug of war began. Sometimes the boulder being dealt with surrendered so easily that it would come careering downhill as if pursuing old 'Chitta-bang', and we would have to steer round quickly to avoid being clouted by a gambolling hunk of granite.

The choice was not an enviable one: slew round on the steep face and hope, heart in mouth, that the tractor would not tipple over, or continue on a straight course downhill pursued by a stony giant, obviously infuriated at being jerked awake from the sleep of long centuries.

On the gentler slopes the work was hard but at least easier on the nerves. We would exhume each great boulder and drag it to the top of the steep face, release the chain and roll it over the edge, letting it bound madly away until it came to rest with a shuddering crash against the old boundary wall.

At last the day came when we had cleared all visible boulders, and we could start ploughing. We made a mark, that is we ploughed a shallow furrow, the length of the hill, running along the top of the steep face. Then we started ploughing one way down hill.

We used the Ferguson tractor for this, with the hydraulic lift. Almost immediately we ran into a serious snag. In normal work with the Ferguson at plough the lift system was a tremendous advantage. Not only could we lift the plough out of the work when we reached the headland, at the touch of a lever, but if we encountered an obstacle, a boulder or a root which fouled the plough, then all we had to do was to reverse and back clear.

It was a very different matter when ploughing down the steep face. We kept encountering hidden boulders and often the plough-share ran well underneath before we noticed the drag or it stalled the tractor. The problem then was how to reverse up the almost vertical pitch and get clear enough to lift the plough out of trouble.

The first time this happened I nearly panicked. It was no fun being suspended, tractor and man, upon the great meat hook of the plough. I couldn't reverse, and I wondered whether or not the weight of the tractor would eventually dislodge the rock and lurch downhill, despite the brake, whilst I was trying to loosen the offending obstacle with the crowbar I carried on the tractor.

I used to slide gingerly off the tractor, block the wheels with large stones, and set to work. Occasionally I could loosen the rocks by raising and lowering the plough with the hydraulic system, but this had to be done very carefully as it would have been easy to strain the frame of the plough.

I don't know how many shares we wore out or lost on that hill face, but the local smith did well out of us. It was with great satisfaction that I drew the last furrow and we turned our attention to ploughing out the top of the hill.

3. *Sudden Storm*

I enjoyed ploughing the rest of Barney Hill, though the weather had broken and not a day passed without sudden storms sweeping down from the mountains. We fitted a cab on the Ferguson tractor which sheltered us from the stormy winds and driving rain. From the cab window I would watch the long ribbon of brown plough stretching ahead of me, backed always by the colour-changing mountains; now softest rose by morning light, now distant bluebell hue, or violet-shaded wreathed with fleecy cloud.

Sometimes the mountains lay like hewn coal against the wind blue sky. Then the rowan leaves would blow grey, showing their backs to the wind, their red berries shining as if varnished in the wet light.

A curtain of rain would sweep across the Cree estuary, to banish the creaking thorn and hide the tormented rushes; dousing the flames of jostling whins bedecked with their yellow stars, obliterating the tumbled grey walls and rubbing out the chalk marks of the white toy-sized farm buildings far below.

Gone were the white gulls following after, and unable to see my mark I would halt the plough and wait, boxed in the little cabin with its streaming windows, listening to the rain thrashing against my puny house of tin.

Just as suddenly the curtain would swing back and there below me would be the green Moss, veined like a leaf, with silver salt sea channels, and the blue Cree estuary running to meet the distant Solway Firth.

The thorns would be green below me again and the gulls would reappear, white wings ready to dance again at the wedding of man to earth, and on I would go, ploughing the long furrow, through the white steam rising from rain-wet soil, with my world once more lying bright and new about me.

4. *A Smell of Rain*

'There's a storm blowing up, David,' said Mr. Jamieson. I looked out across the green in-bye pastures, to the rough rush-grown uplands strewn with grey rocks, and the dark whinbushes which clung tenaciously by their twisted, knotted, brown root fingers to the hungry earth. Kissing was still in season, for golden flowers still shone from the angry needles of green. The marginal land ran up to rim of sky and the sharp black line of the moor. Above, the sky hung blue and cloudless apart from a fist of cloud upraised above the heather waste to the south-west.

'What makes you say that?' I asked.

'Look over there,' said Mr. Jamieson. 'The Galloways are coming off the hill.'

At first I had difficulty in spotting them, but sure enough a line of black cows was moving slowly but steadily down towards the white clustered buildings of the farm, the white-banded Belted Galloways of which we had six flashed white in the moving line and helped me to pick them out.

An hour later yellow storm light filled the farm hollow, seeming to be pressed down by black lowering clouds. Rain bucketed down, beating the pond below the farm-yard into a turmoil of frenzied water spouts, and steaming off the rain-plastered hides of the cattle huddled under the high stone walls around the buildings.

It was still raining after milking and as I turned the Ayrshires out into the home pasture, I saw the Galloways streaming back towards the moor, steam rising from the plodding herd. 'The Galloways are going back to the hill,' I shouted across the yard to the Boss.

'Yes, David, I saw them going. It'll be a fine night. I reckon they can smell the weather.'

5. *Millions of Bugs*

'Blasted people.' Mr. Jamieson came into the byre with a face like thunder. 'They're sending the milk back again. That's two days running. What the hell are they doing at that creamery? Sixty gallons down the drain.'

My heart sank. Mr. Jamieson saw my face and hastened to reassure. 'I'm not getting at you, lad. We've gone all this time with no trouble whilst you've been washing up the machines.' He turned towards the dairy, which was set about twenty paces from the byre.

'Come on,' he said. 'Let's go through the cleaning routine again to see if we can spot the trouble.'

We checked and rechecked without coming up with any obvious flaw.

'What about the milk churns?' I queried.

Mr. Jamieson scratched his head, propping himself against the sink. 'The creamery sterilise them before they come back to us, and since we had that row they don't sling the empty churns down any more but place them on the milk stand, with the lids on!'

'I wonder if the "roadies" have started helping themselves again?' I murmured half to myself, as I worried for an explanation.

'No, David, that's not the answer this time,' rejoined the boss. All the churns were affected and every one was up to the ten gallon mark, when they reached the creamery.'

We sat there pondering. The noise of scrubbing came to us from the cooling room. 'Who's that?' I asked.

'It'll be Jeannie from the croft,' said Mr. Jamieson. 'The wife asked her to come up this week to help with the butter making. She'll be scrubbing the tables down.'

An unearthly screech rose from next door as Jeannie started singing, it sounded rather like two tom cats having a battle royal, only more so.

We continued our inspection of the dairy equipment, wincing occasionally as Jeannie reached for and crashed through the sound barrier. 'I think I'll ring the creamery and ask them to send a "lab. wallah" to take swabs,' said Mr. Jamieson at long length. He turned to go into the

168

house. It was then we heard Jeannie's voice reach new hitherto unexplored realms of rapture but accompanied this time by a strange booming, resonant sound. 'Come quick,' beckoned the Boss. Together we peered round the cooling room door. Jeannie was bent head first into one of the empty churns, screaming and booming away, no doubt quite intoxicated by the sound of the music.

'What is she doing?' I breathed in an awed whisper.

'Scrubbing them out,' said the boss, as if he himself couldn't quite believe it.

'Come out of that, Jeannie,' he bawled, banging on the side of the churn. Jeannie shot out like a cork from a bottle of well matured wine.

'Dinna fash yersel,' she cackled, waving her scrubbing brush under Mr. Jamieson's nose. ''Tis only claining 'em I am.'

'Don't you ever touch the churns again, Jeannie. You've put millions of little bugs into those churns and that's why the milk has been sent back. Leave them to David and me.'

We went up to the house for 'ten-o-clocks' and afterwards as I made my way back to the dairy, I saw Jeannie peering into the churns, a look of bewilderment on her gaunt red face.

'Millyuns o' bugs — bloody leear! I canna see un!'

6. *Moss of Cree*

I had walked further than I had realised and the clunk and spurge of black sea-water running back to fill the tide-sucked ginnels made me turn and head for home.

The restless clamour of geese out on the mudbanks had bewitched me and stolen the time. As I turned, the wind from the North stung my face, making me bow my head and shove my hands deep into my greatcoat. The mountains were deepest blue against the breast-of-bullfinch sky. There was a sparkle and tingle of frost in the knife edge air. Drifts of pink sea-thrift had long since withered paper thin and brown, but the sky gave back the flower colour to the marsh, and lit the water plashes with a wash of pink.

Northward the mountains were black, and the sun in dying lit the snow-tipped peak of Ettrick with silver brilliance, as brief as it was bright. The skirt of sky above the estuary's mountain thighs was now the palest blue and in its paling picked again the water flowers from the marsh.

I reached the firmer ground beyond the reaches of the tide as the ground light left the marshes and above me the first stars pricked the dome of sky. I stopped in my tracks, catching my breath at the sight of shifting rainbows above the mountains. The Northern lights, soft-coloured bands of hazy light, growing and receding as if they played upon the mountain peaks.

Behind me the voices of the geese were drowned by the roar of beating wings as skein after skein lifted from mud banks, bound for their feeding grounds. The geese were already high as the skein passed over me, the beating of wings drowned by the wild beauty of their calling.

I turned and headed for home, thinking of the fireside, a mug of tea, a good book and, of course, my pipe, to round off a perfect day.

7. *Blackface, Greyface*

I must confess that I never felt really at home with the sheep at Cairn Farm, perhaps because of my years with Southdowns.

With the breeding flock of Blackface and Greyface ewes I felt rather as though I was driving a horse which kept slipping its bit, so that I was never really in control.

We used Border Leicester tups on the Blackface and Greyface ewes: the latter were Border Leicester cross Blackface ewes, and they comprised about half the flock.

The Greyfaces were wonderful mothers, they milked well and combined all the good qualities of both parent breeds. The resultant lambs from mating again with Border Leicesters matured quickly and made good weight when graded in the late Summer, but we never used them for breeding. The first cross between breeds brings what stock-men call hybrid-vigour, but with the second crosses there was always a greater risk of recessive genes coming together, resulting in poor quality stock. Not only this, but we had to guard against breeding out the strong Blackface charac-teristics, with their talent for standing hard weather and rough grazing.

Each year in September time we bought in about thirty Blackface tegs, these were last year's ewe lambs, ready for breeding.

I shall never forget the first bunch of Blackfaces I saw brought on to Cairn farm. They poured out of the cattle wagon like a troop of cavalry. Curved horns, splashed with red paint, a common method of marking. Bright black eyes which flashed in the sunlight as they raced into the pas-ture. They wheeled round with the swiftness of a starling horde to turn and face us from a spur of rock at the far end of the field. I swung the gate shut at a sign from Mr. Jamieson. The clatter of the gate against the post, had the effect of a pistol shot and away the tegs raced again. The dyke round the field was strong and high, they went over it like a band of Scots on a raiding foray over the Border. I could amost hear their war-whoop, and see the tam-o'-shanters, and the swirl of the kilt with their plaids flying behind them.

It was some weeks before they settled down in their new home and joined up with the flock. In late October we 'put the tups in' and the ewes and tegs had other things to think about.

The Winter that followed was hard. Heavy snow in early January was followed by a partial thaw, followed again by frost, then more snow. We lost count of the number of snow-thaw-frost cycles. One could see at a glance what the pattern of weather had been when we cut into a snow drift. The exposed face looked for all the world like layer upon layer of sedimentary rock. White for snow fall, grey for thaw and black indicating the tight clamped jaws of frost.

We were feeding the ewes in this weather. Each morning we took out a trough feed of ewe cakelets and crushed oats. We had no hay racks, so we fastened some old hurdles along the dyke and packed the space with sweet hay.

The Greyface ewes fed eagerly, also a handful of Blackface ewes, but for the most part the wild 'Blackies' sniffed at the troughs and walked away to scratch hopefully at the frozen earth. Even the sweet hay failed to tempt them.

Day by day the Blackface ewes got weaker. I told Mr. Jamieson that I would try spreading food on the ground away from the other ewes, to see if they might start to feed. 'You can try it Davey, but don't be too hopeful. Those creatures have picked and scratched for a living all their lives. They just don't know what a good meal is!'

He was right, apart from a few half-hearted nibbles at the cake and pulls at the hay, the Blackface did not feed. They lived or rather eked out an existence on moss, and frozen moss at that. Some got so weak that their fleeces froze to the ground as they lay at night. Their body warmth partially melted the snow beneath them but it froze again as the water ran out into the long wool of the fleece. In the mornings I had often to drag them to their feet.

Just as things were getting really desperate the wind ran back into the West and the thaw came. This brought relief on the one hand, for the Blackface were able to roam and feed again, but danger on the other, as the ditches on the moor and marsh foamed and boiled with the rush of flood water. We lost several sheep, which drowned as in a weakened state they went to drink and stumbled in. Once in the gullies they stuck — the sides were far too steep for them to try to clamber out, and once below the level of the surrounding moor or rough pasture they were quite invisible. Usually it was weeks before we found them.

Lambing time began in the middle of March. The ewes were brought into Whinney Field near the farmhouse. The high stone dykes afforded valuable cover from wind and rain, in addition to which three rocky outcrops crowned with whin were scattered like dark islands upon a sea of light green pasture.

Mr. Jamieson 'walked' the field before the daylight was

spent and again at first light. In between times the ewes got on with it themselves.

I can't say that I was happy with this way of shepherding; my time with Southdowns had conditioned me to being with the sheep pretty well all the time.

At Cairn Farm the kitchen was my domain. After supper I was left to my own devices and through the long winter evenings would sit by the old kitchen range with my pipe and a good book, wanting for nothing; but when lambing started I could not sit easy, the old restlessness would come over me and I had to be amongst the sheep. I used to take Mr. Jamieson's lambing torch, with its great beam which could drive a golden swath of light through the darkest night, and walk out into that strange fascinating world which lies between sunset and sunrise. Once amongst the sheep the peace would come back. I knew Mr. Jamieson was right when he said 'The old Blackface can look after themselves.' They, like the Galloways, were still nature's own children and more often than not they only lambed a single. Still, I liked to be there, and on occasions was able to help a teg with her first lamb into the world.

The Border Leicesters threw larger lambs than a Blackface would and often a teg, hardly aware of the strange thing that was happening to her, would push the head of her lamb into the world and finding blessed relief after the first pains of the head being born, would stop working, get up and wander off. Sometimes she would try to steal another ewe's newly born lamb, quite unaware that her own lamb was slowly strangling.

There were often times when a ewe lambed down right in the open, and the new-born lamb would be exposed to the driving rain. Then I would draw the ewe under cover of the dyke or one of the islands of whin. The difference in temperature had to be experienced to be believed — it felt an overcoat warmer.

If a ewe was in labour before midnight I stayed up until she was finished. Mr. Jamieson laughed at my fussiness but it was kindly laughter. He knew only too well the worth of twenty lambs saved.

For myself, the wakeful broken nights were redeemed

when I could watch a ewe drop twin lambs and walk away with the stronger of the two and know that if I had not been there, another lamb would have been found wet, white and lifeless and for no apparent reason. Again it was the work of seconds to catch a teg wandering aimlessly about with her lamb half-born, and to draw a foreleg forward and ease a lamb into the world alive and well.

8. *Blind Ewe*

Talking about wandering reminds me of a ewe that I once found on our moor in high Summer. To the casual observer, she was just a ewe going about her business. I saw her as I sat looking over the moor behind Duck Hill. She was passing in front of, or rather beneath, a gale-battered and twisted thorn, moving from left to right. I saw her and dismissed her. I was far more interested in the merlin perched on the thorn. A quarter of an hour later a sheep appeared to my left and passed below the thorn branches of the bush. The merlin streaked away like a blue bullet and returned again empty taloned to his perch. Time ticked by, again the sheep passed the tree, from the left. The merlin dipped low over the heather and was lost to sight against the light and shade of the moor. I walked down to the thorn, the sheep track was worn brown and shiny with the passing of hooves, and without much thought I followed it. The track ran full circle back to the thorn and an old grey ewe passing it, blind and unknowing for the umpteenth time, marking each journey with a few more strands of wool caught upon the thorns, as she walked herself into the grave. She was driven by a need to find and be with the flock.

I told Mr. Jamieson and he went up to the moor and put an end to her searching.

9. *On Duck Hill*

Above me a kestrel hung upon the wind, wings finger feather splayed and barred tail fanned to catch the current of warm air uprising. I moved to ease my body as I lay on the green turf on the summit of Duck Hill. The hawk swung pendulum away and disappeared around the shoulder of the hill.

He would be coming back, strange things were happening in the rabbit burrows just below the ridge, within a few yards of where I lay. The kestrel had been back and forth all morning, a silent vibrant sentinel, watching and waiting.

It was late May, the green forest of bracken already unfolding, soon to bring its cool green Summer darkness to the turf and hide, until another Spring, pale primroses and purple violets. A flash of white caught the corner of my eye. I slid a glance towards the burrows, a male sheldduck was just emerging. I had seen these ducks before but his splendid plumage always made my heart beat faster. Red bill, bottle green head and neck, snow white plumage with its rusty orange band encircling breast and upper back.

He turned and looked back down the burrow, making low agitated noises — duck stage-whispers. Nothing happened and he disappeared again. A few seconds later he emerged and repeated the performance. This went on for at least a quarter of an hour, his stage whispers growing louder and more insistent, as if he were fed up and had thrown caution to the winds.

At last I heard other sounds, thin high plaintive 'peepings'. The drake moved to one side of the burrow and peered down, his voice taking on a distinctly wheedling note. Then out they came like a trickle of hot cross-buns, one, two, three, four, tiny ducklings, to be almost knocked flying by a further jostling bunch of four, desperate in their anxiety not to be separated from their fellows. Behind them came the duck, no doubt the cause of the undignified haste of the reluctant ducklings.

The ducklings were off-white, with lead grey bills and feet and a sepia cross from head to tail and across the shoulders. They stood blinking beady eyes in the strong sunlight, undecided, bewildered, all 'peep' and big feet. The drake was in no mood for dawdling, almost two miles lay between his brood and the safety of the friendly marshes of the Cree estuary.

They were away down the hillside in a bobbing, weaving line, the ducklings seeming to move in short breathless rushes. The duck brought up the rear, now fetching out a wayward youngster 'lost' behind a tuft of rushes, now urging on the slow-coach of the family.

The hawk soared over the skyline, rising again to hang upon the sill of sky, but he was too late. I rose to my feet and he planed away. He would keep looking, for those sharp eyes knew as well as I did that the sheldducks were on the move.

Over to my left the Galloway cattle were making their unhurried way across from Barney Hill, striking a line that would cut right across the route of the sheldduck pilgrims, but the ducks were on their own now and the unheeding feet of Galloways were perhaps the least of their troubles.

10. *Sundew*

I spent quite a lot of time on Duck Hill, keeping the sheep off the new ley we had put down. Mr. Jamieson and I noticed the amount of wild white clover which grew wherever the bracken gave it room and light. Our experience on Barney Hill was strong evidence that Duck Hill also consisted of glacial debris and much rich soil. It was as if some giant had tipped an immense barrow load of garden soil in the middle of the moors and we were determined to use its potential to the full. We had bashed, rolled and harrowed one side of the hill, until the bracken had been eaten into submission, and then I had spent the best part of a day 'fiddling!' The seed fiddle was both simple and ingenious. Grass seed was carried in a stout linen bag, slung around the shoulder and fed into a square box fiddle, there were holes in the base of the box and the seed fell onto a vaned disc of metal fixed upon a spindle and rotated by a leather thong fixed to the fiddler's bow.

The fiddler walked up and down fiddling and broadcasting the seed as he went. The grass had taken well but the sheep were quick to find the tender crowns and were grazing it too hard. A certain amount of grazing was good for the grass, encouraging it to tiller, that is to put down its roots. On the other hand too much grazing destroyed the grass cover of the soil and given a dry time the exposed soil would dry out too much and we would lose the grass altogether. The grasses would run up to flower and seed in a last desperate attempt to perpetuate themselves in reproducing their kind by seeding rather than by vegetative growth spread.

This then was my job, to allow the flock half an hour's grazing and then, with the help of Potter and Moses, to put them back onto the moor and to keep them there. In between times I mended gaps in the stone dykes. By the time dinner-time came round Moses had tired of the job and had as usual gone 'walk about'! He was a well-known figure at most of the farms in the immediate neighbourhood. He was young and handsome and it was after all Springtime!

At lunchtime I sat with my back to the grey rocks and looked out over the moor. Potter the black collie, faithful as ever, lay at my feet, his amber eyes never leaving my face. The sun was hot upon my back and white 'bishops' or 'bee-skeps' sailed across the calm blue sea of sky. Across the Cree the great mountain wall of Cairnsmoor rose up to shoulder the sky. Today Cairnsmoor looked far away, it's colours changing as cloud shadows momentarily dappled its flanks and moved on. On a Winter's day when Cairnsmoor slept beneath the blankets of the snow, it would loom large and menacing. At those times it seemed as if one could throw a pebble from our back door onto its great white side. A redshank flew up from the moor, crying hysterically, but no hawk swung in the quiet sky. Potter, who had cocked his ears at the calling bird, dropped them again and relaxed, the moor settled back into its noon-day slumber.

A bluebottle zig-zagged out of nowhere and settled upon the toe of my boot. He was warm in the sun like myself and well content. I wriggled my boot and he zoomed away, only to return again. I thought of the moments of delighted distraction bluebottles had given me in many a chapel when groaning under the weighty burden of a protracted sermon. The times I had wondered just which 'Sunday go to meeting hat' the errant bluebottle would alight upon next. Again I wriggled my boot, and away he zoomed, this time the bluebottle selected a seemingly more attractive though regrettably permanent resting place, a sundew. The damp moorland was red with their hairy rosettes of spoon-shaped leaves. They sparkled like jewels as the sun caught the dew drops which adorned each red hair. The bluebottle decided to change its position. It moved a tentative leg, nothing happened. The fly remained unperturbed, it had after all five more legs. It tried again, nothing happened and the fly became distinctly worried. The bluebottle was, of course, trapped, the sundew bedecked with jewels was a death trap. All the tugging of legs and whirring of wings was to no avail and as I finished my lunch the sundew closed its leaf over the helpless fly and got on with its own meal.

11. *Hay Time*

The methods we used were traditional but the means varied. Everything depended upon the weather. If the weather held fine with a good drying wind the haymaking went like clockwork. The grass was cut, then the swathe turner came in to flip the swathe over, and given good weather we would begin that very same day putting the hay into mows, the name given to the tall pikes of hay, which held enough to fill a trailer. We used to cut the grass fairly early, concentrating upon good grass with a high protein content, rather than wait until the grass had run up to full flower. This had many advantages, the swathes, though sappy, were thinner and therefore cured more quickly. One turn with the swathe turner was normally enough and this meant that less of the precious leaves were knocked off the clover. In any case too much turning and messing about meant dusty hay which had lost its nose —

the sweet smell which is the mark of well made hay.

When the hay was ready to put into mows we used the buckrake mounted on the rear of the Ferguson tractor and swept it into great rings. Then Mr. Jamieson or myself would stand in the centre of the circle of swept hay and begin to build the mow as the other pitched. It was fascinating work, the builder worked round and round the mow, placing each pitchfork full and treading the hay down as he went. The vital factor was to keep the middle full, a principle that applied to all rick-building whether large or small. Higher and higher the mow grew, until it was time to put the cap on, which usually consisted of rough substandard hay. Then the mow was combed down with a hay rake to ensure that any rain would run straight off. The greater part of the hay crop was carted off and lodged in the barn at the first opportunity, but once in the mows the hay was safe for weeks and would take no fault.

We only had the one barn at Cairnhouse farm and therefore much of the hay had to stay in the field until the barn needed replenishing. These mows were usually built in a double line as near to the field gate and protecting dykes as possible. Their caps were thatched with rushes and two ropes secured at each end with a large stone, were thrown over at right angles, to hold the cap on. It was not a long job on a Winter's day to nip out to the little stackyard of mows and bring one in on the trailer. At any rate that was the theory, getting the top off a mow in strong wind could be a bit hair-raising. It was always a relief to work one's way down and begin to feel the warm shelter of the other mows.

One day an incident happened that taught me how much one takes for granted the simple skills one has learnt. I suppose that over the years they become a part of oneself, almost second nature. A friend of the Jamiesons came up for the salmon fishing, there was nothing unusual in that, but when I was told that he was a Lt. General my eyes popped a bit. Mr. Jamieson laughed at me, 'Don't you worry, David,' he said. 'You'll find him good company. Anyway, he's insisted upon working a bit each day.' Mr. Jamieson looked at me with a suspicious gleam in his eye. 'I've asked him to help you to bring a load of hay in from Whinney Field tomorrow morning.'

So be it, I thought, as we rattled and bumped our way out to the field. The General started off sitting in the bed of the trailer. He soon stood up and hung on to the ladders with which the trailer was equipped. I felt a bit guilty, but it had seemed so obvious to me that the most painful place to sit was the hard, bouncing bed of a trailer — especially travelling on our rocky tracks. There again there was no need for him to dance about even when standing. Why on earth didn't he straddle his legs slightly and bend his knees to cushion the shock. I slowed down and he looked visibly relieved. The General was a nice fellow, but he wouldn't hear of me pitching the load of hay from the mow. 'A bit of work will do me good. You load the trailer. I'll give you the hay.'

I am not given to disobeying Generals. We took most of the morning bringing the one load in. Mr. Jamieson nearly had a fit, until I explained what had taken place. The General had pitched into that now as if he would lift it and himself onto the trailer with one triumphant heave. He didn't, instead a tremendous groan broke from him and six strands of hay floated down onto the trailer bed. It went on like that for two hours. I pleaded with him to let me pitch. 'I started this job and I'll finish it,' he said firmly. It was all very commendable but rather pointless. If only he would listen, I thought, getting madder and madder inside. The pitchforks of hay lay in ordered concentric rings, as smart as his men on parade, all one had to do was to lift them off. Virtually no physical effort was required until the load on the trailer became higher than the mow, even then the rhythmic curving and uncurving of the body and arms supplied the spring and thrust needed to lift the forkful of hay up.

We got back to the farm, I was perished with the cold. He, the General, was sweating like a bull, his countenance fiery red. He came down to lunch with both hands bandaged and thereafter stuck to salmon fishing.

That night we all went to the pictures in Newton Stewart and sat in the one and sixpennies. We had fish and chips in the bag afterwards. He was a fine man — just in the wrong seam, as the miners say.

12. *The Farming Calendar*

This was not something which one could buy and hang upon the wall in the farmhouse kitchen. There was no exact date for ploughing, sowing, haytime or reaping. The seasons were roughly the same, although it was jokingly said of the North country that we had three months' Summer and nine months' Winter! The right time for carrying out the different operations on the land — in crop and animal husbandry — varied greatly, it depended upon both terrain and climate. It is difficult to pin down just how the system worked in any one area. When working on great estates one hardly saw one's neighbours. We worked as an independent unit and before the complete mechanisation of the farm we always had enough labour to cope with the tasks as they arose. The Manager made the various decisions, guided if he were wise by the advice and information given to him by the Wagonner, Stockman and Shepherd. He probably never admitted this to anyone but himself and the old farm hands were far too wise to presume to offer direct advice. The Waggoner would just mention in passing that 'the beans in The Lizard were getting a bit Winter proud' that is, making too much top growth, and the Manager would tell him a couple of days later to 'Go and harrow those beans in the Lizard.'

When building a hay rick in rather showery unsettled weather, old Durrant would casually mention that 'There's a fair bit of fire grass hereabouts Gaffer' and again the Manager knew that the rick was in danger of beginning to overheat. 'Better put a chimney in, Durrant,' he would say. Fire grass was the name given by the older men to the ribwort or narrow-leaved plaintain, which holds quite a bit of moisture in its leaves, and a chimney was the method of setting a chaff-bag full of straw in the centre of the rick and then gradually raising it as the rick grew higher, thus forming a chimney up through the middle of the rick to allow the heat to escape.

In Galloway as in most hill country, the system worked differently. The farms were generally small family units and they depended very much upon the good will of their neighbours. Old Henry, looking out of his door one May morning, would see and hear his neighbour rattling and jingling his hay rake down the lane towards the blacksmiths, and by mid-day perhaps a dozen hay rakes would be surrounding an irate blacksmith, all needing some form of urgent repair before hay-making. 'I've been sittin' on me backside all Winter, most days, wi' nowt ter do an' now this,' he would storm, waving his hands at the dumb machines and their equally dumb and contrite owners. 'Will ye never larn.'

'Saddlers have started their corn,' Sally would say as she arrived back home on the school bus, and harvest had begun in the valley. Saddlers had farmed in the valley for five generations, successfully too, and this naturally carried great weight with the neighbours.

Mr. Jamieson's neighbours were very sceptical about his farming methods. He had come over from Aberdeenshire and was very much an incomer. When we first started to make silage the talk ran down the valley as quick as the burn. Now and then a silent figure appeared at the gate of the little stackyard, looked stolidly and silently at the pit we had made, and departed with the wave of his stick. I heard more of the comments when shopping in Newton Stewart or when at the mart or market with Mr. Jamieson. 'Waste o' gud grass; wouldna like my beasts ter eat that owd stuff. I've no doubt that the Boss knew as well as I did what was being said, but phlegmatic as ever, he would only say, 'Time'll tell David.'

Making silage was not easy, for we had no depth of soil and below lay solid rock. We built two parallel walls and faced these with cement, arranging it so that we could drive straight through with the tractor, carrying a load of green silage behind on the buckrake, and dumping it just where we wanted on the heap. After the first day we waited until the temperature had risen high enough to start bacteria working and then got on with the job of filling the clamp with silage. After each layer of silage we sprinkled the green spongy surface with a diluted solution of black molasses.

Work at the silage clamp became hectic and four men from the Displaced Persons Camp came to help us. Only one of them spoke English to any extent and naturally he became their spokesman. One day Mr. Jamieson lost his temper and berated them for spending too much time over their lunch break. They remained sullen and silent until he had gone off to the field to mow some more grass, then the spokesman, a tall dark-featured man, turned to me, with a sad smile 'You people forget that your peace was bought at the cost of our country and our home.' They came from Latvia and Lithuania, part of Russia's slice of the European cake.

When the clamp was finished it rose quite a height above the walls and we laid a road of railway sleepers over it and rolled backwards and forwards with the tractor to consolidate the silage. The less air that got into it the better the silage would be. I had one dodgy moment when I ran over the edge of the roadway and was left tilted at a very precarious angle. Mr. Jamieson helped me off the tractor, which he propped up with two sleepers, and then we rebuilt the road across the wall of the clamp to ground level and gradually inched the tractor on to it and so down to safety. Finally we covered the whole clamp with empty fertiliser bags, then the sleepers and whatever rocks we could lay our hands on.

The silage was a success and we had the satisfaction of several of our neighbours coming up to ask for advice. Our milking herd of eight Ayrshires did very well on the silage and we had virtually no waste, the outside silage was discoloured rather like dark chocolate but still sweet from the molasses and the Galloways and sheep ate as much as possible. The only thing I disliked was the terrible smell, which followed one around for days like a close and devoted friend. Mr. Jamieson was delighted, for the yellow, sometimes almost green, silage which smells the worst is the highest in protein content.

At times of crisis one got a true appreciation of the worth

of good neighbours. If anyone was laid up or the victim of a sudden accident a neighbour would turn up to do the milking. They didn't have to be asked, they just came. One afternoon Mr. Jamieson and I were working desperately to save a field of hay. We had little time to get it into the great mows, but if we could get the hay into small cocks we would save much of it. The sky was black and ominous, not a leaf moved in the long sycamore wood, the dark trees looked as if they were waiting. I glanced over the fields to the white-washed farmbuildings, they had a strange yellow light about them. The air was so charged with the impending storm I felt the hair on the back of my neck prickling. 'It's coming, Davey,' yelled Mr. Jamieson, pointing over to the wood. I looked and saw the backs of the sycamore leaves begin to show as a sudden wind lifted them. Equally suddenly there were six people — men and women — in the field working with us. They brought their own hay forks and boundless energy and as if by a miracle we saw the cleared field and mows standing, great golden statues in the storm light, safe under the falling rain.

13. *The Moor*

The Moor, we never called it anything else, consisted of one hundred acres of wild barren nothingness. Beautiful in August with the purple of heather wine spilt upon it. Lit with a strange warmth in September and October when the bracken became a ragged shawl of amber and gold. The rest of the year it seemed black and inhospitable. On paper it supported thirty Galloway breeding cows and the Blackface ewes. We knew that it didn't and couldn't do any such thing. When the Ministry Inspector came we obliged by putting the stock onto the moor. The Inspector would walk to the top of the Cairn near the farmhouse and gaze knowingly at the Moor lying black and grim in the distance, cluck his approval, and wander back into the house for a cup of tea. During my time at Cairn farm not one Inspector dirtied his shoes in the bogs which starred the moor, those Lilliput jungles of green, red and gold mosses.

During the months I paid many visits to the Moor and it became for me a paradise peopled by plants and creatures large and small, a haven of peace, a place of contemplation.

After work on Spring and Summer evenings I would eagerly head for the moor. Almost daily I discovered new wonders. It was here that I first found the flowers of the cranberry, pink and set upon thread-like stems, resembling miniature cyclamens. The yellow islands of petty whin, set in a sea of purple ling and the pink bell heather. Amongst the rushes of the marsh I found the austere white, green-veined flowers of the Star of Bethlehem. Rank upon rank of white feather-starred spires marked out the humble bog bean, contrasting with tall stands of purple loosestrife and the golden star clusters of the bog asphodel which shone from the singing marsh.

One of my favourite vantage points on the Moor was Duck Hill, a green, rock-strewn, bracken-clad mound, which pushed above the surrounding heather strands and rushy bog land. It was a small edition of Barney Hill which lay to the East just beyond the boundary of the Moor.

I must have spent many hours lying upon the close-cropped turf, watching the orange-rumped mining bees busy amongst the purple thyme and yellow hawkbit suns. Below me the plumes of cotton-grass seemed to float like tethered clouds, bobbing and nodding in the West wind. Grey curlews loosed silver bubble music from their sickle bills to run upon the wind. Then high above me that fan-tailed aeronaut, the snipe, would check his dizzy descent with frenzied bleating, only to ascend again with spiral flight, until he became an eye-bewildering speck, poised for yet another display.

I never reached Duck Hill without being spotted by the keeneyed redshank. There always seemed to be one curt-sying and dipping in red-legged anxiety upon the boundary wall, then at the last moment lifting and leaning back upon the hand of the wind, to disappear in a wicker of brown and white wings, crying hysterically 'Pee-bee-bee!' 'Pee-bee-bee!' 'Pee-bee-bee!' I knew then that it would be some little time before the silence flowed back again around me and the wild creatures would be reassured of safety.

14. *Beware the Galloway*

The Galloway herd and the Ayrshires stood at opposite ends of the husbandry spectrum. The latter were highly bred and any heifer failing to give eight hundred gallons in her first lactation left the milking herd. The Ayrshires looked and were aristocrats, they lived well — not for them the rough grazing and the high moor. When the sun had lost its warmth and the Autumn gales had swept away the dying leaves, then the Ayrshires lay in the warm dry byre, with fragrant hay to pull at and straw beneath them. They would lie there, their brown and white coats sleek in the lamp light, turning now and then to regard me with calm dark eyes, their jaws moving back and forth as they chewed the sweet cud.

Not so the Galloways, by day they would be roaming the tumbled acres, grazing even the beds of rushes. Standing hunched and resolute, backs to the driving wind. During the Winter we carried silage to them, and whole sheaves of oats. The Galloways would string out in a long black bobbing line, eager for the grub which they shared with the geese that flew out from the farmyard each morning we took the oats out. At night the cattle would lie in the lee of one of the high stone dykes. If we had had rain all day and the Galloways could not get a dry lie, then they just stood all night. There was a grandeur about them, not the picture postcard Highland cattle sort but a solid dependable steadfastness.

In late February and March the Galloways calved down. A cow would wander off and make her bed in the bracken and without any fuss she would drop her calf. When she had cleaned and suckled it, the cow would rejoin the herd to graze, moving back to the hidden calf at feed time. This was the stage when the Galloway was at her most dangerous. We never tried to see the calves until the dam deemed it the right time to bring her calf to join the herd. I once foolishly went too close to a new calf lying in the bracken, the cow rushed at me with a tearing bellow of rage and, unlike a bull, she kept her eye upon me, chasing me hither and thither until I was well out of range of her calf.

As the days went by the number of young calves increased. They looked a picture with their black curly coats and smoke-blue eyes, and I loved to watch them as they skylarked about on the fringe of the grazing herd.

I suppose that the grazing cows must have found them something of a nuisance at times, for I would often see one cow with some dozen or fifteen calves around her, quite a distance from the main herd. After an hour or so, another cow would draw back to the bunch of calves and the 'nursemaid' would go off to graze again, with the herd. I don't know whether or not this was general practice amongst Galloways, but I saw it happen several times with ours. Perhaps it was just a local custom!

We only handled the Galloways twice in the year, that was at castrating time, when we 'cut' the bull calves, and on the occasion of the tuberculin test when all cattle including the Ayrshires were tested.

At castrating time all the calves were sorted out from the herd in the pens near the 'fank' or sheep dip. Then amidst a pandemonium of blaring the calves were run through the stocks. Heifers, of course, ran free, the bull calves were checked in the stocks and two bars slipped in behind them, so that they could not back out or lash out. Then the operator slipped in behind and cut the calves with the bloodless castrators, which left no external wound but severed the cords only. The man responsible needed to be cool, quick and efficient, for the longer a calf was penned the more frantic it became.

On the day of tuberculin testing the Vet. came and all cattle had to be caught and held, whilst the Vet. snipped two patches clear of hair on the side of the neck and injected two cultures of tuberculin, avian tuberculin in the top mark and mammalian below. Three days later we had the second round-up and the Vet. measured the skin reaction with his calipers, and recorded the result. The point of the two injections was that a cow infected with avian T.B., which is harmless to human beings, would react markedly to the avian culture, but very slightly to the mammalian culture, whereas a cow infected with mammalian T.B. will show a slight reaction to the avian culture but will react strongly to the mammalian T.B. culture. The avian T.B. culture provided a check when the

Vet. was comparing the skin thickness measurements before and after the injections. Animals infected with mammalian T.B. were, of course, potential carriers of the disease to other animals in the herd and, more important, could transmit the disease to human beings.

It was always an anxious time, until we knew that we had a clean herd and that none of our stock had to be slaughtered.

Each September the Galloway calves of the year went to the mart for sale. They were sold as 'strong stores' and were bought by farmers on the lower ground for fattening. We had no room on our farm, all the good pasture being needed by the dairy herd. For a time the Galloways bereft of their calves would stand about calling and yearning for their offspring, but eventually they would move away to graze and forget, till next September.

15. *Harvest Time*

Our only cereal crop was that of oats. This was the first crop we took from Barney Hill. I thought back to the time of sowing. We used an old-fashioned star drill, which was virtually a box, sixteen feet long and fourteen inches wide, the base of which was drawn almost to a point. A long spindle rotated by the one central wheel of the drill ran the length of the box. This spindle carried star pointed cog wheels set at regular intervals along its length, each wheel opposite and running within a feed hole. The box was filled with seed corn and away we went, dropping the corn on top of land which had been diced and harrowed in readiness. One thing had to be remembered when sailing along on the tractor: the drill was sixteen feet wide and when turning on the headland one needed plenty of room. I only forgot once and spent the whole of that particular lunch hour mending the tow bar which had snapped like a carrot — stone walls are not to be argued with. I also spent most of the following Saturday afternoon repairing the six-foot gap I had made in the boundary wall.

Immediately after sowing, I harrowed the field. There

was no time to waste for it was already black with rooks. The steep slope was broadcast by hand and later, at harvest time, we cut it with the scythe and tied the sheaves by hand.

In the days before harvest, I spent a lot of time cutting rushes in the marsh. We would need all we could lay our hands on for thatching the ricks. It was a job that I loved. We had already thatched the hay rick in the rick yard and needed enough for perhaps three more corn ricks. There is something wonderfully satisfying in putting natural materials to use. It may be the persistent ghost of the primitive past of which we are a part. Dry-stone walling I loved and spent many happy hours repairing gaps. The walls of Galloway are very different in character from the Northern Dales or the Cotswolds. I think that Galloway walls or dykes are far more difficult to build, many of the stones, being glacial debris, were rounded, rubbed smooth by the slow grinding of the ice and other stones, they varied in size from small footballs to side tables. Again and again I marvelled at the strength of the men who, long ago, had heaved these great boulders into position in the dykes. It was commonplace to see a mosaic of smaller stones built snugly around one of these monsters. Mr. Jamieson used to say that 'They ate more porridge in those days' and I can well believe it. The dykes had only one face, unlike the Cotswold wall, for the stones didn't lend themselves to that kind of building. The Eastern boundary of the farm marched with part of the old Edinburgh to Whithorn road, and the boundary wall which traced its course was built of rough dressed stone and double faced. I suppose it all depended upon the stone available in the immediate vicinity.

For cutting rushes I used a Scottish scythe, which differed from the English equivalent in having two handles. The main shank ran up from the butt of the blade and had one handle set in at the top, for the right hand, and the second shank sprang from it about a third of the way up its length, and finished level with the main shank. Again, this had a handle set in the top for the left hand. A wooden strut joined the two shanks near the top to give strength and stability. This wooden Y with the blade attached, looked most ungainly when compared with the sweeping flow of the single-shafted English scythe, but I came to like it and found it easy and uncomplicated to use. It was certainly ideal for cutting tough rushes and bracken, we always built a small rick of the latter, for it made dry comfortable bedding which could absorb plenty of moisture. I much preferred it to hard shiny straw.

We built three small corn ricks, rounded rectangles with low-pitched roofs, which seemed to crouch, as if they were trying to keep out of the wind. Thatching began and having served my apprenticeship upon the hay rick, Mr. Jamieson let me get on with the job myself. He followed me as I finished each rick, securing and stitching it. I started at the end of a rick, working from top to bottom, or ridge to eaves, moving from left to right across the rick. I used to lay a couple of bundles of rush along the ridge and peg them well down, then push my handlefuls of rushes under these fixed bundles, smooth down with my hand and push my next row of bundles under the first row, smooth down again to remove any loose rushes, and move down to the next row. On reaching the eaves I moved my ladder along and started pegging down my ridge bundles for the new section. I was thrilled when I finished my first rick. The green rushes provided a thick waterproof thatch and looked most attractive.

In broken weather we used to put a rough covering of bracken on the corn ricks and secured it with ropes and stones, until we could get round to thatching. Mr. Jamieson used to say that there was no point in 'thatching the rain in'.

Securing and stitching is my own term for the method which Mr. Jamieson used for fastening down the thatch. I had never seen it done his way before. We first threw two strong jute ropes at right angles over the rick (that is, one over the middle and one along the ridge) securing each end to a large anchor stone. A third and fourth rope, looped round the central ridge rope, was slung over each end of the rick to hold it down. These were also secured to anchor stones. A vital point had to be borne in mind regarding the latter — they had to 'hang', not rest upon the ground. Checks were made from time to time, for as the rick settled the anchors would settle with it and if the roof was to remain immune to the tearing gales, it needed the full dragging weight of the anchors.

Mr. Jamieson went even further than this in his guardianship of the precious ricks. He ran a rope right around the rick just below the eaves, taking in the main anchor ropes, and tied it firmly but with just enough tension to allow the main ropes to hang freely. The next stage involved tying lengths of binder twine from the ridge rope down to eave rope which encircled the ridge, these thinner strands were about a hand span apart.

Finally Mr. Jamieson set to work with his home-made needle working round and round the rick from top to bottom, stitching in and out of the loom he had made. The needle was like a three tine fork, the two outer tines running to a single point at the end. The centre tine was shorter and carried the binder twine on a running line looped round it. The method was simple — the needle was pushed under the downward strand and was then withdrawn leaving a loop projecting beyond it, then the needle was passed through the loop and pulled tight and so on to the next strand. The end result was neat, attractive, and most important of all, efficient. The rick secure in a fishing net of thatch. Perhaps the foregoing description seems somewhat pedantic but the corn harvest was vital to the economy of the farm. Winter stretched before us unseen and unknowable, the chances were that we would get through with little trouble, but one never knew. The sight of the mows with their caps of rush thatch, and the neat hamlet of ricks in the stockyard, gave a warm feeling of reassurance. It is no wonder that thatchers of old perched their straw cockerels at each end of the roof ridge, to shout defiance at the demons of darkness, flood, fire and the terrible snatching fingers of Winter's hell hounds.

16. *Hammer-Mill*

We were very proud of our tractor-driven hammer-mill. It was a tremendous asset to us and we used to put whole oat sheaves through it, to make a coarse meal for the trough feed of sheep and Galloways. The hammer-mill could cope with anything apparently, but I was very surprised when one Autumn day, Mr. Jamieson handed me a pair of gauntlets and some garden shears. 'I want you to cut as much whin as you can. Then gather it up on a chaff sheet and bring it down to the mill house.' My face betrayed me and the Boss laughed, 'I know it sounds mad, but I've been reading that gorse is rich in protein and I want to see what sort of a job the hammer-mill will make of it.'

The result was a green spongy meal which we mixed with the dry oat meal for the Ayrshires. Our problem lay in the fact that it contained too high a water content to keep, without some method of drying it. Later on we levelled a square of old whins and as the bushes sprang back into life, we were able to cut them with an old mower. It was an interesting exercise, but not practicable on a large scale, without a crop dryer.

17. *The Day of the Unicorn*

Ayrshires carry beautiful upswept horns. They look very attractive from a distance, they set the animal off, as country folk say. Herdsmen live in terror of them, they know only too well the damage a vicious upswing of those beautiful horns can do to another cow's udder. It is a sickening thing to see the work of two years completely ruined by a flash of temper. Young heifers, newly joining the herd and being shown their place by the older matrons, were most vulnerable. We decided to dehorn the cows ourselves. The practice of dehorning was in its infancy then and various methods, now illegal on the grounds that they caused unnecessary suffering, were being practised. We had already adopted a method of disbudding the calves. As soon as the buds of the horn appeared, we used a caustic solution to kill the growing horn. Great care had to be exercised, for if any of the solution ran into the calf's eye, blindness could result, apart from being extremely painful. There was another hazard in the method, if the solution was applied incorrectly without covering the whole bud, then a horn would still grow. It would be stunted and grotesque in form but still potentially a dangerous weapon. Later on we used the electric hornmaster, whereby an electric current was passed through a metal cap which fitted over the horn bud, this became a very safe, efficient method, and was widely adopted.

Cows presented a different problem. One afternoon I found Mr. Jamieson in the dairy, cutting old teat-cup liners into rings. 'Young Linfoot down the road gave me a tip this morning. He's dehorned all his Ayrshires with these.' He pointed to the growing pile of rubber rings upon the table. 'We'll just slip them onto the horns tomorrow morning after milking.'

'How long does it take?' I queried. 'Won't it affect the milk yield?'

'Well,' said the Boss thoughtfully, stubbing his chin. 'We've got to take a chance. We can't afford to have another torn udder like Cynara's; she's pretty well lost the use of one quarter.' Cynara may seem rather a high flown name for a cow, but all the cows in Mr. Jamieson's herd, which was really quite small, had names beginning with the letter C. By the time Cynara arrived we were running out of names. Crocus and Cowslip were left far behind and we had knitted our brows into the realms of Christabel and, of course, Cynara.

The next morning we put the rings on, rolling a ring down to the base of each horn. The idea was to cut off the blood vessels that nurture the horns. As far as we knew from the experience of Mr. Linfoot, the process took about a fortnight to three weeks. The cows were finally adorned and away they went into the field. The first morning we noticed a lot of head shaking amongst the cows but one couldn't say that they were in pain, from all outward appearances, but there was no doubt that they knew that something was wrong. The milk dropped slightly for three days and then began to pick up again. A fortnight later I picked up a horn near one of the dikes and by the end of the third week twenty-three horns had tumbled. We found them here, there, and everywhere, from cowshed to the far pasture. There was little or no bleeding when they fell and with the aid of ointment dressings the flies bothered the cows very little, in any case we had picked a time of year when even Scottish flies were scarce.

You will have noticed that I said twenty-three horns, the reason was this: by strange trick of fate, Cynara, the shy, the persecuted, whipping girl, of the herd was left with one horn triumphantly intact, 'the sole survivor of a stricken field'. Cynara, the Unicorn, as we nicknamed her, had a field day. For three glorious days, she was undoubtedly the boss. The only consolation lay in the fact that Cynara did not realise that she only had one horn left and in any case she had never been vicious. I rather think she enjoyed the experience of the other cows giving her the right of way for a change. Mr. Jamieson chewed the problem over, saying very little, which was his way. On the morning of the fourth day, during milking, he announced his plan of campaign. He was standing by Cynara as he spoke. She, in blissful ignorance, regarded him with great brown soulful eyes. 'The horn is only hanging on by a thin sliver of bone,' he said, 'and now, of course, the rubber band has no tension at all. I reckon it just needs a tap and off it will come.' I looked at the unicorn, 'hanging' was hardly descriptive of that shining, swept back scimitar.

'Some tap,' I snorted. 'And who is going to tap it. I can't see Cynara standing still while we take pot shots at it!'

'David, have you no faith?' laughed the Boss. 'This is what we'll do. Go and get the beetle and stand behind the door of the byre. I'll let the cows out and as Cynara comes past. . . .' Mr. Jamieson raised both arms 'Bonk!'. . . . . 'and don't miss. You won't get two bites at the cherry!'

I waited apprehensively outside the cowshed door, it was a sliding door and I had left just enough room for the cows to pass through one at a time. I held the beetle — the large wooden mallet we used for driving fence posts — in my sweating hands. Cynara was last out and I swung the beetle in a scything arc, catching the horn fair and square. It snapped like a carrot and Cynara, giving a great bellow, reared up on her hind legs and pawed the empty air, rolling her great eyes. It was all over in seconds and Cynara walked out to pasture with the others, pushed and jostled as if they knew. I looked at her later in the morning. She was grazing quietly and there was no bleeding at all. The day of the unicorn was over.

18. *Death of a Galloway*

Nan was very old and very tired. She was the oldest of our breeding herd, one of the few Belted Galloways we possessed. She stood now in the dried brown fog of the rough pasture that 'marched' with the main road to Wigtown. So frail and light had she grown during the past Summer, that the wind rocked her body this way and that, as she stood on splayed uncertain legs and looked at us, the white of blindness frosting her smoke-blue eyes.

We knew that Nana would not see another Springtime, the long Winter stretched before her and it was one Winter too much.

Slowly and patiently the Boss and I had guided her shaky steps down from the high moor. We had to be practical, for the 'knackers' lorry would never get up there for her, and the moor is a bad place for burying. Apart from that, the purer the spring water that fed the farm, the better.

At last we reached the level terrace of green springy turf near the road gate. Nan stood looking back to the long blue line of the moor, it lay beyond the reach of her old eyes, but she lifted her nose to take the loved scent from the wind. Behind her the burn sang, hurrying now that the sea was so near. A dipper came to sing from a rock splashed white with his droppings. He sang amidst the joy of water, the song the water had taught him and his forebears through the long centuries: bright, sharp, water sweet notes to the hurrying, tumultuous, small thunder of the burn. Sun caught the grey limbs of the rowan which overhung it, the red rain-varnished berries of Autumn shone bright. The Boss raised his gun and fired. Nan swayed once, sank to her knees and became one with the patient earth. Before the echoes of the shot had died away and blue smoke was still whiffling above the rowan tree, a black crow flew from the hill and circled the scene. His pitiless eyes saw everything and though he flew away over Broken Field we knew that he would be back. I only hoped that the lorry would come before the crow returned to perform the last rites, but it didn't.

19. *The Smallholding*

We got the news the day Rob came striding across the Moor to us. We were busy carting stones off Barney Hill and saw him long before he reached us. Rob farmed a smallholding on the other side of the moor, it was far too small to support him and his growing family, but somehow he scraped along. It was perfectly natural that he should spend the first twenty minutes talking about anything and everything before coming to the point. 'Going right round the field before coming to the gate' was what country folk called it. Rob joined us in throwing stones into the trailer. 'This ole wind'll dry the top off the land I'm thinkin' Mister,' he remarked.

Mr. Jamieson answered as if Rob was an everyday visitor to our farm, rather than someone we hadn't seen to speak to for a twelve month. 'Aye, Rob, we must get on with the sowing as soon as we can.'

Stones thudded onto the bed of the trailer, it was warm under the sun. We all stopped for a moment and straightened our backs. The light shimmered and danced above the brown soil, its brilliance hurt our eyes and we automatically lifted them and found rest in the stillness of the moor. 'Can stones breed?' asked Rob, as naturally as he would ask for a match for his pipe. I bent hurriedly to work to hide my grin and heard the Boss's answer come slow and serious.

'That's a good question Rob, it certainly seems so. The

more we pick and work the ground the more there seem to be.'

I glanced up, the Boss wasn't laughing, he had answered the question with the same seriousness as it had been asked: that was typical of the man, always courteous, never patronising, it was no wonder that the hill men held him in high regard. An incomer Mr. Jamieson may have been but he held the key to any countryman's heart, a deep love and understanding of the land and a great respect for the people that lived on it and off it.

At long last Rob arrived at the 'gate' and asked his question and even that was approached obliquely. 'I heard tell that Cockton's leaving "Lovesome"'.

'Is that so?' said the Boss quizzically. I sensed a quickening of interest in his voice and glanced up at his face. The old fox was giving nothing away though and the stones continued to thud into the trailer. Rob was determined to have another chew at the bone.

'Folk says that he be set on moving out Whithorn way.' The Boss grunted non-committally and Rob continued, 'Place is run away to nothin' I grant ye, but ye'll no be arguin' that it 'ould be a big 'elp to 'ee.'

The Boss straightened up, pushing his old deer stalker back as he ruminatively scratched his forehead and gazed towards 'Lovesome'. 'It's hardly more than marsh, whinney bushes and broken-down dikes.' He fished out his faithful half-hunter and gave it a glance. 'And it's dinner-time Rob.'

The fell man turned, 'Aye, I'll be getting back o'er the hill meself. See yer.' He strode off with never a backward glance.

Dinnertime was never leisurely at Cairn farm, the food was good and plentiful but time was always in short supply. It was a case of 'Shut up and sup up'. During my first months I had suffered much from eating too quickly, but one had to eat up or go out hungry. After twenty minutes the Boss would push back his chair, stride out of the kitchen and off across the fields to work, and he expected me to be with him. I would bolt a last mouthful and race after him, praying that the pains in my stomach would go away.

This day was different, I was still laughing inside at Rob's question, 'Do stones breed?' My face must have betrayed me for Mr. Jamieson looked across the table as his wife filled our plates up. There was a gleam in his eye, 'I knew what's tickling you my lad, but don't you ever forget that men like Rob have more wisdom in their little fingers than you've got in your whole body.'

'But stones breeding,' I protested.

Mr. Jamieson laughed. 'I know what you think. On the surface it seems ridiculous, but it goes much deeper than that. You see, to the true countryman, nothing is dead and inanimate. Perhaps it is because modern sophistication has not yet infected men like Rob, that they seem to be still linked to the long ago days when men first farmed. They felt God to be in all things — the hills, trees, rivers, and the very soil they walked upon. God was the life-giver, therefore all created things shared in that life. Now who is to say that they are wrong. When you think like that and still have a sense of reverence and wonder for the world about you, the question Rob asked isn't so daft is it?'

It was quite a sermon for Mr. Jamieson and it shut me up very effectively for the rest of the meal.

Two days later the Boss took me on one side and asked me if I would be prepared to live at 'Lovesome'. I was flabbergasted. 'Oh, I haven't got the place yet David but I'm in the running. We need more ground for the stock and their boundary marches with ours across the Moor.'

I was thrilled at the prospect. The single storey farm-house and outbuildings at 'Lovesome' were solidly built and in pretty good condition, the future was bright indeed. I began naturally, though it turned out unwisely, to make plans myself.

20. The Incomer

The new owner of 'Lovesome' was not Mr. Jamieson, and our boundaries remained unaltered. To make matters worse the incomer was a cardboard countryman. We heard that his parents from the city had bought the place for him, a fact which explained the high price it had been sold at. Our first sight of the new owner was unforgettable. I was washing out the byre after turning the cows into the pasture when the Boss appeared, his face had the look of complete disbelief. 'David,' he said. 'Put that broom down and come and see this.' I walked with him to the top of the cairn and he pointed up the lane. 'The new owner,' he breathed. Down the lane with a click clack of hooves came an eye-dazzling outfit. A black pony in silver and black harness drawing a smart, spotless gig, painted bright yellow, black wheels and yellow spokes. Crowning all the Incomer, resplendent in bowler, loud check suit and yellow suede waistcoat adorned with silver buttons, white shirt and dickey-bow tie. One yellow gloved hand held the reins with obviously uncertain grip and the other flourished a silver-mounted whip.

Neither the Boss nor I said anything. As the Incomer passed our gate, he looked towards us and, with a slight acknowledgment of our existence, touched his bowler with his whip.

A week later his pony clattered down the lane again but on this occasion the gig and its owner were absent. The pony was in full harness and Mr. Jamieson and I stopped its gallop. We returned it to 'Lovesome', apparently the Incomer had been all set for another royal progress to market but had omitted to fasten the harness tugs to the gig. A flick of his whip and the pony had obediently set off, neatly ejecting his owner as the gig tipped forward on its shafts.

The weeks slipped by and the broken walls on 'Lovesome' remained unmended. Visitors up the lane increased but little work got done in the fields.

The Boss asked me to stay on with him and said that he would build a cottage for me on his own land, nearer the main road. A long wait lay ahead, apart from the jungle of planning consent and approval of plans, etc. I had my own plans and being young and impatient could not wait and after talking long into more than one night, Mr. Jamieson and I agreed that I should look elsewhere for a post with a house.

My thoughts turned to the Cotswolds which I longed to see and I applied for a job as shepherd/stockman on a farm on the hills above Winchcombe in Gloucestershire.

For the last time I walked the bounds of Cairn farm, it was early April and there was still snow on the tops. Peewits were turning pied feathered cartwheels, diving and swooping over the pastures. As I climbed the brown whale-back of Barney Hill a host of curlews rose up and wheeled away, their liquid bubbling cries tugging as ever some chord within me. I counted seventy of them as they dropped down towards the marshes. Two oyster catchers beat overhead and called to each other with that sweet melancholy, which seems to be present in all bird voices of the lonely places. I walked the salt marshes and saw a raft of seventeen whooper swans. They were restless, now and again one would stand in the water and beat its snow-white wings. The music of wild bugling broke from them, as they moved away from me, proud straight necks crowned with their lovely slim heads and tapered yellow, black-tipped bills. It was time for them to be gone to the Northern sea-board of Russia and Finland. When they lifted white wings for the last time above the dark hills, they would take the snow with them and Spring would be with us again, but I knew that I would be walking different hills myself by then.

COTSWOLD SPUR

1. *Roel Hill*

I came to Roel Hill Farm on a day when the wind was having a Spring cleaning. Like all good housewives she had two a year and this was the second.

White cloud birds flew from out the wild Welsh hills and dappled the slopes of the Clee with racing shadows. Sycamore leaves which bore the black spot of Autumn were torn in ragged urchin hordes from the Devil's Shaking Tree, the towering sycamore which stood in splendid isolation above Roel Gate. This lonely crossroads was old even before the Saltway was worn and widened like a long furrow across the brow of the green Cotswolds. It had been trodden by the countless feet of packmen, muleteers and the solid wooden wheels of oxen carts, carrying their precious salt from 'Dirty Sheds' or Droitwich, as we know it, to the abbeys, farmsteads and hamlets of England.

The Saltway ran through Roel Hill and straight across the fields to Hawling, but West of it and roughly parallel following the escarpment from the crossroads northwards to the top of Sudeley Hill ran the White-way. I grew to love this lane with its feast of coloured vistas; tumbled woodland, sweeping down, patterned corn fields curving to valley bottom, leading the eye to tree-bosomed Sudeley Castle and the red and brown roofs of Shakespeare's Winchcombe.

Across the valley rose the dark shape of Humblebee Wood, crowned in turn by the form of Belas Knap, the long barrow which had seen the rising and setting of countless suns.

The history of man was cupped within the brown palms of this green-fingered valley. I knew it, felt it and loved every part of it, the days only serving to deepen my sense of being at home.

Below Roel Gate a tongue of green pasture jutted out into the valley, a British camp had been sited there, now marked only by low grass grown ramparts and the ring of circular depressions that marked the corn pits of the first farmers. These were originally lined with straw, but on being emptied had been used as rubbish pits.

I used to stand within the old encampment and look up the valley towards Sudeley Castle. Spoonley Wood lay not half a mile from me and hidden deep amongst the jostling elms, sycamore, ash and chestnut trees lay a Roman villa. It was strange to think that once upon the terraced hillside grew the vine, that Romans walked the colonnades of Spoonley villa, enjoyed the hot baths and traced for the thousandth time the colours and patterns of the tessellated pavements.

I thought of the long sunset when the Romans departed and villas were sacked, burnt or slowly surrendered to the arching bramble and moving roots of encroaching trees.

The Danish war parties had come up the valley and burned Winchcombe Abbey to the ground, and in the churchlike beauty of the great barn of Spur farm the ribs of the little boats that defeated the Armada of Philip of Spain, lay landlocked, upended, beams for the arching roof of the lofty barn. The old numbers burnt in upon them by shipwrights of another day were still plain to see.

This then was the countryside I had come to, rich in natural, man-fashioned and historical wealth.

2. *The Partners*

Roel Hill Farm was owned by two maiden ladies. Having said that I suppose that you have already formed a mind picture of the said ladies! Here were no scions of the front parlour, partaking of afternoon tea, be-laced and with an armoury of knitting needles, but two women, direct opposites in character, gifts and appearance, yet perfectly complementary to one another.

The farm at the time of taking over, was practically fenceless, a wasteland of 300-odd acres, almost a thousand feet up on the Cotswolds. A former tank-training ground with little to commend it to a prospective tenant —

particularly if he or she anticipated farming it 'from the bedroom window' as the saying goes.

The domestic side of things, which included poultry and what dairy work there was, fell under the watchful eye of Miss Pullen. A watchfulness that was at the same time unobtrusive. One always felt that Miss Pullen was there, a sort of local universality like the grass of the place.

I saw much more of Miss Gill, each and every day she worked on the farm. She could turn her hand to making a five bar gate or tackle the job of milking a heifer for the first time, when anything could happen and often did. When we rebuilt the Dutch barn after fire had left a mountain of smouldering ash and twisted girders, Miss Gill was there helping us to raise the great telegraph poles of wood and later I remember her perched like a red-capped starling on the roof ridge, nailing on the sheets of corrugated iron.

The stock were my prime responsibility — one hundred heifers which we reared from the bucket and sold out as down calvers and also a flock of some fifty Kerry Hill ewes which we crossed with a Suffolk ram.

The incident which I remember most vividly was connected with the sheep. It happened during lambing time. The ewes were gathered by night in the implement shed, which we had lined with straw bales. They had plenty of room and were snug and warm. Generally speaking the Kerry Hills were easy lambers, they had ample room for their young and by using Suffolk tups we were assured of small fine heads on the lambs, which of course aided delivery. On this particular night as midnight approached, three ewes began to 'make their bed'. I knew then that I would be up until the light came. Two of them lambed down without any trouble, but the third ewe, though trying desperately hard, could not lamb on her own. After giving her plenty of time I decided to intervene, there was no point in letting her exhaust herself. The lamb, a very large single, was coming backwards. I delivered it successfully but was concerned to see that the ewe continued straining.

She took the lamb and began to clean it, licking it eagerly with her rough tongue. Reassured, I turned to have a last look around the flock. All was quiet, at last I could snatch some sleep before milking time was upon me. I went back to the ewe I had helped, to see if the youngster was ready for a drop of milk. What I found appalled me. The ewe lay stretched out, the lamb still at her nose — twitching in its efforts to rise. The poor ewe had thrown her womb (the lamb bed) right out.

Within seconds I was hammering at the farmhouse door and Miss Gill appeared. Hurriedly I told her what I needed, then dashed back to the yard. Miss Gill did not waste time, she was suddenly there at my elbow, with a bucket of warm water, disinfectant, empty bottle and an old sheet stuffed into a plastic washing-up bowl.

'What a mess,' was all she said. 'Can we save her?'

'I'm not sure,' I said. 'Old Edgar once told me how to save a ewe like this. We'll have a go. After all we haven't much choice — leave her and we lose her.'

I took the empty lemonade bottle and dropped it into the bucket and left Miss Gill adding the Dettol, whilst I hurried to the cowshed to wash my hands.

Arriving back we tore the sheet in half and spread it by the ewe, then lifting up the womb I held it whilst Miss Gill poured over the warm water from the lemonade bottle, washing away the bits of straw, etc. and then we laid it upon the clean sheet.

Now came the most difficult part. Miss Gill had to hold the ewe upside down, gripping the hind legs tight. I lifted the ewe up and Miss Gill took hold. She didn't flinch and as she held the ewe I gently eased the womb back, it was a delicate job, rather like folding back a stocking that was inside out, starting at the toe end.

When it was replaced I inserted the bottle leaving the neck end protruding and finally stitched above and below the neck.

Miss Gill looked a little pale but I never admired her more than I did that night.

A few days later I cut the stitches and retrieved the bottle. The ewe recovered and settled down nicely and, wonder of wonders, there was no infection.

3. *The Terrible Silence*

A car rattled and bumped its way into the grass grown farmyard, lurching to a halt before the farm cottage. My father and mother emerged after what seemed an eternity, as if they could not believe that they had at last arrived. He, now grown bulky in his city suit and black tie worn on all occasions, his mane of grey hair blown awry in the eternal wind. My mother, all seven stone of her, looking like a wisp of thistledown caught momentarily against a dry-stone wall. I had heard the car approaching whilst mucking out the calf pens and now I pushed open the door and went over to greet them.

'Trust you to come to the world's end,' said my father.

'Don't you find it lonely?' asked my mother as we went into the cottage for tea.

I couldn't linger over the meal, having to dash back to get the cows in for milking. 'Have a look round,' I said, 'and I'll be back as soon as I've turned the cows out.'

An hour later I went to look for my parents. I was surprised to see their suitcases still in the car. My mother met me at the cottage gate. 'Your father's sitting in the hay field. We've got to go back. It's this terrible silence. If we don't go I think we'll go mad — it's like a blanket.'

Go they did, back to Sheffield, the smoke and the bearable noise.

I went and leaned over the gate, smoked my pipe and looked out over the rolling Cotswolds and let the silence lap me round. Above me in the vaulted sky the wind plucked plumes of mare's-tail could, combing the white manes free, to stream as silken tresses far across the sky to Broadway tower, stone sentinel which crowned the distant ridge. As ever a legion of larks sang high and poured their sunlit song upon the stone-hemmed barley seas, green waves that constantly beat to break in white fool's parsley foam against the dry-stone walls. Walls which had seen three centuries of summers.

A blackbird came with flirting tail to sing upon the cottage's blue slate ridge and on the hidden roadway high above Winchcombe a motorbike droned, the abandoned singing of its rider, courting bound, rising clear above the machine.

In the pasture below me a brown molehill sat up, raised two long, enquiring, black-tipped ears and loped casually away. The day before I had counted over twenty hares in the clover ley near Paris Wood, soon I must start thinning them out again.

I relit my pipe and my mother's words came back to me, 'This terrible silence', and the need arose in me to somehow try to interpret the country silences so that those that live in the noise and clash of cities might learn to hear again the voice and see again the beauty of the countryside, through ears and eyes made clear by understanding.

4. Dry-Walling

It was a lovely day and, stock work finished, I set off across the fields to join Bill who was already dry-walling, mending the gaps in the wall which surrounded the sycamore wind-break.

Around me the Cotswold country rolled away to Broadway and the blue haze of Evesham Vale. My fingers were still sore from the hours I had spent walling the day before. I thought with some pride of the gap I had repaired, and with that in mind took a line across the field so that I could look at my handiwork.

My pride was shortlived. My piece of wall was down again, a tumble of stones, the gap looking larger than ever. I stood in dejection. Some way along the wall I could see Bill working steadily away. Stooping to pick up a stone, placing it in the wall, stooping again. He seemed to have an easy, almost casual rhythm in his work.

I walked along the wall towards him. Bill straightened up and began to roll a smoke. Beyond him the edge of the Cotswolds fell away into the green valley of wood and farmland, then swept up again into the long line of Humble Bee Wood.

Bill lit up and blue smoke curled up into the sycamores.

'Morning Bill,' I greeted him.

'Morning David,' he replied. 'Come to try your hand again?'

'Aye.' There was a long pause, then I blurted out. 'How is it Bill that when you pick a stone up, you never throw it down again? I can never get mine to fit.'

The old man took another pull at the thin fag and had a long think. 'Well,' he said. 'Reckon I've worked with stones on and off all my life.' Then looking away into the distance he added. 'I love stones, there's a place for everyone in my wall. Anyways, they all come out of it.'

'My wall's down,' I said, as if he did not know. 'Perhaps I didn't go high enough and a cow tried to jump it.'

Bill laughed but there was no malice in his reply. 'If a rabbit had sneezed yer mean. Come on let's go and look at it.'

We walked back to the scene of my efforts. 'Right,' said Bill. 'I want every stone cleared back. Not anyhow mind, keep 'em separate; "firsts" for the outside faces, "throughs" to tie them, and heart stones to fill the middle. Leave the "copings" for the top right at the back.'

Soon every stone was cleared right away. Then Bill fell on his knees and with his great spade-like hands began to burrow down at the base of the old wall. Heap after heap of black earth was scooped out. 'There's yer trouble,' cried Bill, straightening up. 'Come and look here!'

I bent down. One of the great foundation stones had slipped down and was tilted at a sharp angle. 'Get it out,' said Bill. 'Straighten it up and then you'll build. Remember allus get yer foundation right. Build yer outside walls, keep 'em level. Cant them ever so slightly to the middle. Fill in the "heart" as yer go, and use yer "throughs" ter marry the two faces together. Then top out with yer "copings".'

As he turned away to leave me to it, Bill said, 'Don't go trying ter knock pieces off ter make 'em fit. They all came out, reckon they can all go back.'

5. *Man with a Gun*

I had never possessed a gun of my own and when Bill offered me his old single-barrelled twelve bore for the princely sum of three pounds, I closed the deal without hesitation.

Nothing is as simple as it seems, least of all human nature. I loved wild creatures and yet those long evenings I spent walking round Roel Hill Farm with my gun under my arm, were amongst some of the happiest I can remember.

I find the same problem with fox hunting, at the sight of the Hunt and the sound of the lifted horn my pulse quickens. The yarring call of the whipper-in and the statuesque figure of the huntsman in his 'pink' waiting amongst the beeches at the end of the woodland ride, and hound voices echoing from the misty depths of Spoonley Wood, were of the essence of the English country scene.

For all that my sympathies are with the fox as, out-numbered and often outpaced, he pits his wits against huntsman and hound.

In actual fact we had no shooting rights on Roel Hill Farm, at least as far as game was concerned, but rabbits, woodpigeon and vermin were outside the pale and theoretically could fall to my gun.

I say theoretically because Miss Gill had let the shooting rights to a great landowner in the valley. He annually reared hundreds of pheasants to provide 'sport'. These birds, being hand-fed, were so tame that when the beaters were driving the woods, they had the devil of a job getting them to fly at all over the waiting guns.

Our farm was never shot over to my knowledge but with a ring of such farms surrounding the great estate the reared birds had plenty of room and were not reared for someone else to have the pleasure of shooting them.

In a sense Roel Hill Farm acted as a buffer, our crops of kale, roots, rape and the like affording cover and feed for the game birds.

Naturally the sound of a gun up on Roel Hill gave little joy to the squire's gamekeepers. I could guarantee that they would pay me a visit at the cottage that night or at the latest the following morning. The 'bang' of my old gun was the same whether aimed at a rabbit or a plump pheasant!

I remember returning to the cottage one late afternoon; it was snowing hard and visibility was almost down to nil. I was cold and empty-handed, nothing for the pot that night! At that moment over my head came a whirr of wings, a covey of partridges shot low over me. I upped and shot in one movement. Six birds fell onto the snow. They were plump and warm to my hand and were soon hanging in the old larder.

The next morning I had hardly sat down to breakfast when there came a knock on the back door. Opening it the red hard-bitten face of Rudge, the head keeper, was thrust into too close proximity. 'Did ye hear any shots larss night up 'ere?' he rasped.

It was one of those occasions when the truth paid off. 'Yes, gamekeeper,' I answered, my mouth still full of cornflakes.

'Were they close?' he questioned, rolling a red-rimmed eye.

'I'll say,' I rejoined with fervour. 'I might have been standing right next to 'em.'

'See anyone?'

'No, gamekeeper, I can't say I did. Last night in that snow it would have been difficult to see anyone else.'

'Ah,' he muttered. 'Keep yer eyes open.'

'I'll do that keeper,' I said with real enthusiasm. He swung away, apparently satisfied, dogs at heel, and over my shoulder six partridges swung idly from their hooks.

6. *The Call*

Our nearest village was Hawling and it was there we went to chapel. It was almost three miles by road but not much more than a mile and a half across the fields. The lights of the chapel could be seen from the Devil's Shaking Tree and certainly the tree sounded eerie enough when the

West wind was twisting its great branches against the night sky. We were not many in congregation, perhaps fifteen in all, but it was a friendly place to go to. The Minister was called Stewart Denyer, he used to call at the farm when he could, rattling down the rough track on his motorbike. He would stand chatting to me as I milked, always approachable and good to talk to. An elderly Minister, Ezra Kendal, came to preach at the chapel sometimes. He spoke to us in the tongue of the market place. Never condescending yet never shooting his words way above our heads.

I began to go to the weekly fellowship meetings held in various farmhouses. Mr. Denyer had the gift of making the old figures of the Bible live. He put flesh upon those very dry bones and made me see them almost as contemporaries, sharing the same emotions and facing basically the same problems men have faced through all the ages. I knew what he meant, I had often felt the same about the old people when walking round the earthworks of the old British Camp, pausing to look at the sunken saucers in the turf, the marks of the old pits in which they had once stored their corn against the coming of Winter, or picked up a piece of red Samian pottery ware down in Spoonley Villa, filled with wonder as I ran my fingers over the delicate patterns traced upon that old fragment. Romans almost brushed my shoulder, we were very close in the corridor of time.

One day as I worked in one of the great fields looking out over Humblebee Wood and Belas Knap behind it, God came into the field and shouted at me. He shouted that I must 'Go and preach.' All that day He shouted, so that I began to think the great cloud shadows scudding over the broad hills' flank were His footprints.

I've been too long on my own, I thought, hearing voices now of all things. The next day He came again, and yet again, the noise was like that of thunder, yet there was no sign of it in the blue clear air. The sheep grazed in contentment about me, as if it were just another day.

I began to argue with myself. 'It's not as if you're any good. You've tried preaching once, and a fine mess you made of it' and the clincher, 'You're not good enough to do that. Hardly the kind of person fit to preach to others.'

When the fellowship night came round I went determined to ask a question of Mr. Denyer. The time for free discussion came and I was silent. I was perhaps mistaken. There had been no voices, it was all in the mind.

Then a voice spoke from the back of the room. A farm lad in his teens. Haltingly, and red with confusion, he asked his question. 'How do you know when God is asking you to do something?'

My question. I waited, the blood pounding in my ears and heard Mr. Denyer's quiet voice say, 'If it is good, it is God.' That night I asked for a 'Note-to-Preach' and at the next meeting of our Cheltenham Circuit Ministers and Preachers, I was given a Note. This meant that I took three services a quarter, in the company of and with the guidance of a senior lay preacher. He would report back upon my progress to the next Preachers' Meeting.

7. *Kerry Hills*

Each year we bought a bunch of Kerry Hill ewes to replenish our breeding stock, at the same time old ewes were drafted out, usually to be sold for slaughter. We normally bought them down at Honeybourne in the Vale of Evesham. A farmer brought them in from the hills of Montgomeryshire. An old shepherd took me round the various lots and if I liked the look of a particular bunch, he would let them run out and round the old stone courtyard. The first bunch were maiden ewes, few sheep are prettier to look at than Kerry Hills. They looked as smart as paint, with their bright black and white faces and legs. Miss Gill looked surprised when I said 'Put 'em back. I'll take a look at the next lot.' The second pen lacked the lovely pert heads of the first. They looked larger-headed and rangy by comparison. The shepherd said 'they've all lambed as lambs.'

I turned to Miss Gill. 'Those are the ones we want.'

'But surely they've not the quality of the first bunch?' she questioned.

The shepherd intervened, 'Your man's right, Missus. We only let the best grown lambs have a lamb in their first year. They baint so pretty but they're good field sheep an'll do ye well.'

As we drove home, Miss Gill was still unconvinced. 'They've already had lambs.'

I replied, 'Surely that's something in their favour. They'll be no trouble to us next lambing. They'll know all about it.'

'But a lamb in the first year. . .' she protested.

'That's not strictly true,' I reasoned. The lot we bought were born a year last April, which will make them two years old by the next time they lamb with us. You can't blame the hill farmers getting an extra crop of lambs.'

The Kerry Hills we crossed with a Suffolk tup and they did extremely well, our lamb crop average was 1¾ per ewe. We sold most of the lambs for grading, that is slaughter at twelve weeks old, and they scaled eighty pounds live weight. It was great to stand by our pens of fat lambs at the sale, with their broad backs, a bloom on their coats and bright black faces.

8. *Old Thorn*

Where the Saltway left the bracken and struck out along the ridge to run between the seas of barley, grew an old thorn. It's growing days seemed to be over, it had given up the unequal struggle against the nagging wind and stood with hunched shoulders from dawn to dimnity, like an old man waiting.

August that year was a barley grower's dream, the earth was baked and panted crack mouth open, the bracken was roasted brown and crisp. The inevitable happened, some-one carelessly flicked a match and the Common became an inferno. Later I walked upon the warm ashes, the old thorn was a blackened skeleton, still crouching before a non-existent wind.

Harvest came again and every trailer load of straw had an armful teased from its side as it passed the old thorn. I promised Bill that I would take an axe and clear it out of the way, but the promise slipped to the back of my mind and I didn't get round to it.

In Spring I walked the Saltway again, the Common was recovering slowly from the effects of the fire, brambles had already their red clusters of young uncurling leaves, the green stars of bluebell leaves were showing. The thorn stood as black as ever by the track. 'Better out of the way' I thought. 'Next time I come I'll bring the axe!'

May blossom clouds were caught in the hawthorn along the hedges before I returned, axe in hand. I shall never forget that moment for the old thorn had the last word. One branch, the furthest away from the searching hunger of the fire, was smothered in blossom. Not a leaf was to be seen, just a branch of blossom making Spring.

When I got back to the farm with the axe unused upon my shoulder I was greeted by Bill. 'Ye don't mean to say that you've actually been and cut that old thorn down at last,' he laughed. I felt a fool as I told him what had happened, but to my surprise Bill didn't laugh. Instead he turned away from me and looked out across the rolling countryside to Broadway Tower. 'Ye did right, lad. My ole man was a hard one. He never stopped telling me that unless ye made it by the time ye were forty, ye never would. I never made it, whatever that means, an' I ain't bothered. That ole thorn had summat ter tell us all. P'raps that while there's life there's hope.' Bill stomped off to his tractor and I went to see the down calvers in Far Field. As I walked with Joe, my sheep dog shadow, the words of George Borrow came to mind. 'Life is sweet brother. Do you think so? Think so? There's day and night brother, both sweet things; sun, moon and stars, brother, all sweet things: there's likewise a wind on the heath. . .'

9. *Down Calvers*

I struck out across Great Middle Field, from the edge of Paris Wood — we called it that because of the Herb Paris which grew there. The name seemed particularly apt for it was in that wood that I heard my one and only nightingale whilst at Roel Hill. My progress across the young corn was slow; the flinty ground was rich in fossils and I was always on the look out for 'shepherd's crowns' or fairy loaves. These were the fossils of sea-urchins, or echinoids, lying upon the bed of an ancient sea, some 1,000 feet above sea-level. The name 'fairy loaves' dates from medieval times when the cottage wives would put one on top of the oven to assist the bread in its rising. They always seemed to be grouped in the numerous saucer-like depressions which pockmarked the surface of the field. I also found the devil's thunder darts, or belemnites, which the old people believe fell during thunder storms. Once or twice I picked up beautiful bivalve specimens. The limestone was rich in fossils and with the help of the handbooks from the British Museum, I began to have my eyes opened.

I reached the down calvers and gave them their cake and corn from the bin we kept against the gate. Then I perched myself upon the fence and lighting my pipe settled to watch them. It was a clear morning, blue sky with fine wind-spun cirrus twisting into mares' tails which had the sheen of the sun's grooming upon them.

All the down calvers came up to feed, all were bright-eyed with the bloom of health and well being in their thick coats. I made a note of those which showed signs of drawing near to calving. We always brought them in for the last month. We did this for two reasons, firstly to get them used to being tethered and led with a halter, and secondly to give them an extra ration of cake to help them to develop a good udder. This method of pre-calving feeding was called 'steaming up' and like all processes involving living things, the process was 'open-ended'. By feeding abnormally high protein cake, we not only stimulated the development of the udder but we also set in motion before time a whole sequence of events. We found that down calvers were making so much milk that we had to start milking them before they calved down. This had certain advantages for us, in that we had a longer period in which to get the cows used to milking and general handling. On the other hand, in beginning to milk before the calf arrived, we denied it the benefit of the colostrum or first milk. This first milk is rich in vitamins and the anti-bodies which help the calf to fight off infection until such time as it is able to manufacture antibodies of its own. Not only this but the first milk is obviously tailor-made for the calf's very new digestive system and the first few days of feeding are vital in the young life.

When we had a bunch of down calvers coming down within a few days of each other, we always had some colo-strum on hand and could, therefore, switch some to the newly born calf, but this did not always happen and we would then hopefully add cod-liver oil to the calves' feed.

Ninety-per-cent of the calves reared on our farm were bucket fed. Immediately after birth the calf was removed to the range of calf pens, which were warm and snug. It was no good allowing the cow and calf time to build up a relationship. This sounds cruel and in the nature of things I agree, but in the event it would have been much crueller to allow a bond to develop, only to break it within a week when the mother went off to market for sale as down calver. This would have made life a lot more difficult for the folk that had the job of rearing the calves. Just to give one illustration; the calf instinctively splays its front legs and pushes upwards to find the teat, once it is allowed to do this, and experience confirms that its instinct is correct, then it is a hundred times more difficult to convince a bucket fed calf that it must put its head down into the bucket to find the milk that it is so ravenous for. We used to straddle the calf and give it the fingers of one hand to suck, the other hand held the bucket and gradually the calf, busily sucking one's fingers for all it was worth, was drawn down to the warm milk. Nine times out of ten the moment the calf tasted the milk, it would give a tremendous up-ward thrust with its nose, and unless you had your wits about you the bucket and milk went flying. It took a lot of patience to get the calf used to looking down for its milk, once this was achieved the next stage began, that of teaching the calf to drink.

Hand-feeding calves was a time-consuming and painful business. The first point is obvious, the second not so, until you have personally felt the razor sharp milk teeth of a calf chewing the backs of your fingers. I'm not at all surprised at cows lashing out at their over-eager offspring, after all, teats are not made of India rubber.

The second stage of teaching a calf to drink was easier, one gradually reduced the number of fingers being chewed each day by one, until the calf was gulping away happily on its own. The trick was to keep deliberately withdrawing the fingers from the calf's mouth in the hope that it would be so busy enjoying the milk that it would not notice that the fingers had disappeared. Gradually over a period of eight weeks the milk was reduced and a calf meal or milk substitute replaced it. Milk was not always available in the quantities we needed when we were bucket-feeding twenty calves.

I slipped down from my perch, swallows were hawking insects disturbed by the cattle, twisting and turning like black shadows. Some instinct made me look up, just in time to see a peregrine shouldering his way through the great blue vault above us. Out of the corner of my eye I saw the wheatear which had been waiting for me move, slip quietly with a flirt of its white, black-tipped tail, into a cranny of the stone wall. No doubt she had another blue egg to add to her clutch of three. I walked back up the track well content, the cattle were looking really well and prospects at Gloucester Market, barring accidents, were promising.

Miss Gill reared Friesians and nothing else. I had grown to like them, and to realise that they were not just producers of 'blue water'. This was the jibe often made by Jersey and Ayrshire herdsmen. Friesians were capable of tremendous lactations, 1,000 gallons were nothing to them, but it was true that the butter-fat content sometimes suffered, because of the emphasis given to yield rather than quality of milk.

Our system worked very well. Roel Hill farm rose to 1,000 feet, or rather 986 feet above sea level, and the cattle we reared were tough and fit. They were outside all through the year and were remarkably disease-free. The Cotswold limestone grew good bones and we turned out some of the loveliest down calvers anyone could wish for.

Cheltenham — always an attractive centre — had many small intensive dairy farms surrounding it, which found a ready market for their produce. The problem of these dairy herds was that they had no room for rearing stock. Miss Gill used to buy up their best heifer calves, rear them up on our hill, get them in calf by using the Artificial Insemination Centre, and then sell them out as fresh down calvers at about two years and three months old. The calves we kept; the heifers to be reared in their turn, and bull calves to be sold out as strong stores for beef.

The calves we bought in were often from very good pedigree stock and our use of top A.I. bulls could only improve their progeny. When the calf market was slack we had to buy in calves from mothers that were not fully pedigree but were on the supplementary register of the Friesian Society. By using A.I. we were always raising the standard, for the progeny of these calves when fully grown would be recognised as full pedigree. One memorable morning in Gloucester market we sold three heifers at £127, £123 and £128 respectively. They were truly lovely dairy cattle and in 1952 that was a decent price to get. I felt proud to have reared them up, and yet very sad to say Goodbye to them.

10. *The Vet*

We didn't see much of the Vet, not that we didn't like him, but his arrival on the farm, apart from routine Tuberculin Testing of the cattle, spelt trouble and so the less we had to call upon his services the better we liked it. His visits were confined to the cattle. Sheepwise I could manage on my own for our flock of Kerry Hills was never larger than sixty breeding ewes. As I have already mentioned, all the ewes we bought in had already borne a lamb and this combined with the fact that the Suffolk tups always threw lambs with fine black Suffolk heads made lambing easy.

One year we had dog trouble but my twelve bore soon put a stop to that. Apart from my Welsh sheep dog, Joe, we never saw a dog on the farm, apart from the occasional visits of the Hunt. The dog trouble came out of the blue about six weeks before the ewes were due to start lambing. I came out of my cottage one morning to hear the sound of dogs barking and the ewes crying. I grabbed my gun and a handful of cartridges and ran up to the field. Two dogs — a black Labrador and a tiny Cairn terrier — were running the ewes. I yelled at the top of my voice and the odd couple streaked for the far side of the field. I put two shots over their heads, for as far as I could see no ewes had been savaged, only a few mouthfuls of wool lay upon the grass. That was the first and only time we had trouble with dogs on the loose. No apparent damage had been done and yet that lambing was the worst as far as difficult deliveries were concerned. A few lambs were born dead and other ewes needed help because they had been chased and their lambs were misplaced and twisted up in the womb.

Calvings were our most difficult jobs. Bill, the tractor driver, went home to the village at night and in any case he was no stockman. This left Miss Gill and myself to cope on our own and although she never spared herself in the heaving and shoving that calving often entails, her strength just wasn't equal to it. We kept three cows for house use and to provide milk for rearing. These calvings were easy, but all the others were first calvers and time and again night would find Miss Gill and myself struggling in a cramped, draughty, ill-lit loose box trying to bring a reluctant calf into the world. Some of the trouble we ran into may have been due to the bull we chose to use as a donor from the A.I. Centre. We could not always buy in calves of the quality we wanted, but we had as it were, to keep the production line running. The farm depended more than anything else upon the regular sale of fresh down calvers and we just had to make up our lack of first-class stock with calvers that were not true Friesian strain but might have a bit of Shorthorn or Ayrshire in their make up. These, when they grew into heifers, we crossed with a Hereford bull for there used to be a saying that 'anything with a white face will sell in Gloucester market' and the progeny of a Hereford bull always carries that dominant trade-mark. Sometimes we sold these calves out as strong stores for other folk to fatten but often we fattened a bunch ourselves during the Winter, in the two covered yards, within the square of loose boxes and calf pens.

At bad calvings it was always a blessed relief to see the Vet arrive and though he must have hated being pulled from a warm bed, he never said so, but pitched in with us until the job was completed.

Once we had a blue-roan heifer completely off her food and we had to call the Vet in. Miss Gill told him over the 'phone that we thought the heifer had swallowed some sort of foreign body. The Vet said that he would bring his metal detector with him and at about eleven o'clock he duly arrived.

I had tied 'Bluey' up in one of the covered yards and on the Vet's arrival took him down to see her. The Vet was anxious to show off his 'mine detector', as I called it. 'We'll soon get this sorted out,' he said. 'I want you to stand by Bluey's head and listen. The moment this instrument passes over the top of anything metal, the low humming tone will rise to a high-pitched note. Listen to this!' The Vet switched on, immediately the instrument gave a high-pitched note of protest. 'Funny,' he said as he moved the detector along Bluey's flank. No matter where he placed the instrument the result was the same. 'I can't understand it,' said the puzzled operator. 'Bloody cow must be made of iron!' Just then Miss Gill leaned over the gate, drawn by the strange piercing noise. 'Come and have some coffee,' she called and then, woman-like, added, 'You might do better if you moved Bluey from under that tin roof.'

We never did trace the metal object for, as I untied her from the post, she went berserk and fled from the yard, taking two five-barred gates almost in her stride. Bluey smashed the top rail of the first and flattened the second on her way to freedom. She must have decided that to live with her foreign body was the lesser of two evils, for we had no more trouble with her. Until she left the farm for pastures new, we called her the Iron Maiden.

11. *Shearing Again*

Life at Roel Hill was spacious and full. There was always plenty of work to do but time to do it in. I did all my own shearing between milkings and enjoyed the peace and quietness of it all. Each evening I would bring about fifteen ewes under cover for the night. This meant that I could start shearing first thing after breakfast. I used the old-fashioned hand shears which I loved and worked on a canvas which I kept swept clean between shearing each sheep. The less straw and dirt in a fleece the better. I can see the ewes now, cold green-grey eyes watching me intently as I made my mind up which one would be the next customer. The art of catching a sheep lies in one golden rule and that is, never to look at the sheep you want and yet never take your eye off it. One must look without obviously looking, walk amongst the sheep and then suddenly fling out an arm and 'Got yer!' I would pick a ewe whose wool had risen. This was easy to spot for the neck wool always came away first and often stood out like a snow-white ruff. Not only were these sheep easier to shear because the new wool had lifted the old fleece off the body, taking with it the line of body grease, but they were always the fittest or wealthiest ewes in the flock and a plump, well-covered sheep will sit more comfortably and therefore quietly than a scraggy bag of bones. Sooner or later all the sheep had to be sheared but I avoided the poor ones for as long as possible. The quickest way to lose the edge on one's shears was to plough through the thick yellow grease of a ewe whose fleece had not risen. These were the sheep that got cut and nicked by the shears in the process, it was almost inevitable. The skin of a wealthy ewe is firm and tight, and as the shearer bends his ewe this way and that the fleece falls away from his shears and the cutting line is plain. The wool seems to stand out, as if it were ready to spring away from the body.

12. *Cotswold Blizzard*

Most people see the Cotswold Country as H.J. Massingham did in his book 'Shepherd's Country'. Dreaming wolds, the soft bower of flowers, and pastoral heart of England. It is as if Winter never happened, but it does. We awoke one morning to find snow up to the bedroom windows of the cottage. A drift of snow like the great sail of a ship swept from the corner of the building right across the cobbled yard to the long arm of the cow byres. We dug ourselves out and I went to survey the scene. The down calvers were in Hawthorn Warren and well protected by the friendly arm of Paris Wood. I had made a point of spreading bales of barley straw under the lee of the wood, which besides giving the cattle something sweet to pick at, also provided a dry lie. Barley straw used to be fed from racks to yarded beef cattle, but I never liked this practice, barley awns are terrible things for any beast to get in its eyes.

The neat footprints of a fox led across from the wood to the rabbit warren and then away downhill towards the Guiting road. After milking Sue and Cherry and feeding the calves, I went in search of the sheep. I knew that the older ewes in the flock were weather-wise, they knew the ground and would pick the right spot to lie, until the storm had blown itself out. They were running a leg on the hillside, overlooking the valley between Charlton Abbots and Winchcombe, and must have caught the full force of the driving snow. I took a bale of the sweet meadow hay that sheep love and set out. I kept to the middle of the fields for here the wind had not allowed the snow to settle and except for occasional pockets of snow the going was pretty easy, apart, that is, from the icy, unrelenting bite of the wind, which numbed my face and took the feeling from my hands, which clutched the strings of the bale upon my back. The wild creatures had been about their business, the narrow footprints, two and two, left by the bounding stoat, rather the rabbit than me, I thought. When anyone uses the adjective 'remorseless' then I think of the stoat and his smaller cousin, the weasel. They pack amazing energy into those lithe whipcord bodies. A great brown bird broke from the wood as I approached, and the buzzard, for such it was, beat away on its great rounded wings heading towards Paris Wood. Above me the clouds gave way to the bright sun and the snow dazzled my eyes until they ached with the glare. Once through the windbreak of black sycamores and down over the brow of the hill, I was in a different world, and there out of the wind in a sun-cupped hollow lay the flock. I sat on the bale of hay for a moment amongst them, smoking my pipe, and feeling the sun's blessing upon me. Then I broke the bale and gave the wedges of hay to them to pull at, savouring the scent of sweet vernal again, a taste of Spring in the crystal air of a white world. Across the valley the light and shade of snow marked out the ridge and furrow whale-back lands of medieval ploughmen and even on the Spur the sheep-worn ramparts of the old British camp thrust their snow-clad line as if to challenge the valley below. Bugles from the sky brought a joyous tumult of feeling to me and a strange, sweet restlessness as a line of wild swans beat high over me, bearing towards the Vale of Evesham. Even at that height in the clear air I could catch the soughing 'Hompah', 'Hompah' of their white wings. They told me so plainly that I was but an earth-bound man, whose eyes would never see the rainbow beauty of the Arctic Summer, when their wings had finally lifted to take the snow from the hills and they had gone home.

I checked the stock again before the light went, but as I reached the sheep with some more food, I could smell the snow upon the wind's shoulder. It started slowly and the flakes were big and ominous and before I cleared the sycamores I could not see anything but a bewildering maze of turning, twisting snow devils. Up on the hillside the wind caught me again and I lost all sense of direction, save that I knew that by heading uphill, I was bound to strike the long wall over the crest of the hill, that led down to the cottage. The snow was being driven now and felt more like needles of driven ice which stung my face until it ached. At last I topped the last curling rise of the wolds and thankfully crouched behind the boundary wall.

The wind whipped the snow like white sea spume over

the top of the wall where it fell as if bewildered by its loss of momentum, to lie like smooth, white, tide-washed rocks, moulded by an unseen hand into beautiful curves and jutting cornices.

Then a covey of partridges shot over my head on curved wings, plumping down on the snow within a few feet of me. For a moment or two they just sat, then they began to run about like so many clockwork toys.

I moved ever so slightly to ease my cramped position. Instantly they froze and I could see their bright little button eyes watching me intently. They thought they were hidden, but the whiteness of the snow played traitor to them. They were no longer brown — mole hills on a green pasture, or invisible on the brown ploughing, but black like lumps of charcoal against the pure white snow. I straightened up and with a whir of wings they vanished behind the moving curtain of snow and I continued my homeward journey.

Never did a fire seem more welcome, it was good to shut the door and to leave the weather outside.

13. *Last Summer*

It was three years since I had come to Roel Hill Farm and life was beginning to settle down to a familiar pattern. I cannot imagine anyone not liking the Cotswolds, their quiet beauty grows upon one, as season follows season. Countryside that has a contented look, not smug, but conveying a sense of peace and well-being. There is a harmony between man and his environment; nowhere else in this island do houses grow so naturally from their surroundings. Buildings so often are an intrusion, if not an affront, to the land about them, but here it is as if man and nature had achieved a perfect balance, a working partnership. Men may have shaped the Cotswold countryside but I feel that they must have been happy men. Happy because they recognised their true wealth and reverenced the world which lay about their feet.

We grew a lot of barley for malting. Rich land is no use

for that purpose, it give too much nitrogen to the barley and makes the grain 'flinty' which is disliked by the brewers. The great field which lay on the Western edge of the farm, between the Saltway and the White-way, was almost sixty acres. I often helped with such jobs as harrowing but never enjoyed the wide acres. The job became very monotonous and therefore boring. One very warm day I nodded off on the tractor and awoke with a start to find myself heading straight for one of the telegraph poles that took seven league steps across the field. Keeping an eye upon the mark became tiring to the eyes and the rows of twisted green barley leaves seemed endless.

I looked forward to lunchtime when I could shut off the yammering voice of the dusty orange tractor. The bliss of such a moment has to be experienced to be believed. All at once one became aware of the larks' high singing and the corn bunting jangling his bunch of keys as he perched upon the wire fence which ran alongside the White-way. Corn buntings have always seemed to be one of the more deprived species of the bird world. They lack the beauty of the yellow-hammer and are rather brown, dowdy and dull. No such gem as 'A little bit of bread and no cheese' drops from their beaks, only a grating apology which sounds as though the poor bird had perpetual gear trouble. There he sits, back hunched and disconsolate, and when he does take flight, he hasn't the energy to tuck his legs up. Somehow I feel sorry for the corn buntings of this world, perhaps they were pushed to the back of the queue, when gifts and graces were handed out. Perhaps the corn bunting does not need my sympathy. No doubt to another corn bunting of the right sex, he or she, has got everything a self-respecting corn bunting needs.

I always stopped for lunch, when doing field work, as near to the White-way as I could. Whereas the Saltway struck straight across country in a most businesslike manner, the White-way clung lovingly to the contours of the hill. It was as if those that first trod it were determined that they would take in every possible view. Lovely Bredon, the far hills of Malvern, Cleeve Cloud, and sometimes helped by the sure knowledge that they were still there, the blue

226

shadow shapes of the Black Mountains could be seen. Here the pink thimble buds of wild roses at their opening beguiled the traveller and honeysuckle massed its red gold trumpet clusters to blow the sweetest fanfare of fragrance England knows. Old Man's Beard, the hoary bearded clematis, supplied the dormice with feather beds and draped the roadside bushes and trees with a maze of brown ropes and fretted greenery. Birds sang in Spoonley Wood from dawn to dusk until the Spring had spent itself and Summer brought other tasks to be done. All were soloists in their own right, yet never lovelier than when upon an evening in the childhood of Spring they sang as if one to another. Blackbird, slow, sweet, meditative, then a songthrush, always from the same long branch in the tall pine, singing his phrases again and again with quiet assurance. Storm cock, defiant in the Devil's Shaking Tree, shouting shrill to the West wind that he was still here, and the robin's singing on into the half light, as the owls began to call, thin sweet flint splinters of song spinning out into the listening wood, striking sparks from the heart.

That was the magic of White-way, but the Saltway was always a place for hurrying, built from A to B, and for good reason. The old parish roads were set about with toll gates, demanding a tithe upon salt and those who travelled the Saltways dodged the toll gates, avoided paying the tax, but missed the view and much else besides.

Towards harvest men began to arrive at the farm. I would see them walking the farm or else engaged in deep conversation with Miss Gill in the stackyard. 'Mark my words,' growled Bill, with unease evident in his voice, 'there's trouble coming fer the likes of you an' me. An' more fer you, with a tied cottage an' all. Reckon you'd better face 'er with it, David, an' find out what's goin' on.'

The upshot was that the farm was to be sold and though Miss Gill thought that I would be asked to stay, she just could not promise that I would be wanted. As far as she knew, the whole emphasis of the farm would be shifting away from stock.

This decided it for me. I needed stock as a fish does water. One Friday morning in September saw a laden removal van climb slowly out of the Roel Hill Farm hollow. We were going a long way, down to Cornwall in fact, and although I didn't know it then, to find something that would change my life eventually in a way which would have seemed impossible at that moment. On the surface the change was quite simple, my sheep in the not too distant future would have two feet instead of four, and regrettably my dogs would be useless in gathering them up together.

GLYMPTON CHURCHYARD

1. *The Buttery Bush*

Over thirty years lay between the afternoon in Glympton Churchyard and the long journey I had made from the Roel Hill to Cornwall. Edgar and all that he had taught me seemed very close. A thrush came to the elder bush which overhung the churchyard wall and shook the flowers from it and I remembered the buttery bush at the sheep house at Northchurch Farm. This morning I had walked round the old estate before coming on to Glympton. Many years lay between me and the morning I had cut down the buttery bush at Edgar's command. I had felt that it was a lot of fuss about nothing really. I had just arrived at the caravan that morning and was looking forward to a mug of tea, sweetened with some of Edgar's condensed milk.

'Arter brakefus ye can take yon bill 'ook an' cut down that buttery bush behind the sheep 'ouse.'

'Righto Edgar,' I replied, secretly wondering what all the rush was about. The buttery bush in question couldn't have been more than four feet high. His eyes must have read the question in my face.

'Taint verra big as yet but yer wanna watch the buttery bush. Do as I tell 'ee an' cut it down. I want it out of the way.' He creaked away, chuntering 'Much use as toothache!'

I was left in some doubt whether the last remark referred to the offending bush or myself!

As I finished my mug of tea, I thought about the buttery bush, or the elderberry, to call it by its proper name. In hedge and gate country nobody welcomes it — apart from the womenfolk who make champagne from its flowers in early Summer and wine in the Autumn from the great trusses of purple berries.

The buttery bush will soon ruin a thickset hedge. Its wood is soft and sassy. Sheep and cattle have no problem in pushing through it, like a knife through butter in fact.

It was a ten minute job to cut the bush down after

breakfast. For good measure I had splintered the stump into a thousand fragments — until nothing remained above ground level.

Edgar was proud of the sheep house. It was about 20 yards long, built upon brick and weather-boarded. Its strong timbered roof was covered with attractive red tiles. The front stood open, revealing the many pens for the show rams and ewes we reared.

This morning then, I had walked up the overgrown track to look at the sheep house again. The sheep house lay in ruins — the long spine of its red roof timbers broken. The buttery bush towered over, thirty feet high. Edgar had been right to be worried about the stripling buttery bush. Hadn't he always taught me that life will triumph over the world of things, the dead and inanimate things we fill our lives with. 'It's not so much what we are, as what we're becoming, that's important,' he had once said very sagely. 'An' what we are, is allus more important than what we 'ave.'

My thoughts, as I looked at the wreck of the pride of Edgar's heart, went straight to the stripling buttery bush on that rubbish tip outside the walls of the City men called Holy. Christ, too, had been deemed useless — dangerous by some, cut down to size, ground into the dust and forgotten. Two thousand years had gone by, not thirty, and the tree of life was still growing over the broken walls of the pride of Rome.

This is why I knew that I must return to Glympton, if for nothing else than to say thank you for a man that in his way had taught me my ministry, and I had found that because his words had been true they were always alive and meaningful.

Soon I would have to turn from this quiet place and continue my journey amongst my two-legged sheep. I read again his name, so empty of meaning, to the world, yet so wonderfully warm and rich to those whose privilege it had been to be his friends and companions while he tended his flock. The last day that Edgar worked in the fold came flooding back and with it the sense that if true holiness is wholeness then this man knew holiness in the way he lived his life.

2. *The Last Day*

The Summer had gone and harvest poppies long since had dropped their scarlet petals back into the earth, or gathered by the reaper's metal hand lay pressed between the golden sheaves which waited for the threshing drum to draw beside the neat corn stacks. Autumn set a rainbow in the weeping trees and we waited with the ewes for another lambing time.

Edgar still hobbled about, getting harder to please and quicker to spit out a retort. At times the pain must have been intense, although he never mentioned his legs. I knew that he would not retire — voluntarily at any rate — and the Boss knew Edgar too well to mention it. Harry, Old Nodder and I just tried to make it easier for him, without the old man knowing it.

The last day came in November, in a way that was as sudden as it was unexpected. One morning I turned into Gallows Furlong where we were folding the ewes. It was blowing a gale, driving great streamers of rain before it. The wind whipped up my oilskin as I turned the corner and headed towards the shepherd's hut. Edgar was already there as I stomped through the muddy field towards him.

'Mornin' Davey,' he growled as he struggled to hook back the door against the great hand of the wind.

'Morning Edgar,' I shouted against the noise of the gale. 'I'll go and let the ewes on.'

'No ye won't. Git stove agoin' an' mak' the tea,' he snarled.

'It's too rough Edgar — let me do it,' I pleaded.

He was in the hut now, reaching for his crook. 'Dang 'ee Davey, I baint finished yet. I be aroight — make the tea.'

I watched him struggle away across the field, bent against the grey rain, then the ewes saw him and a tumult of baaing was caught and tossed by the wind.

Already the ewes were moving forward towards the new fold, they had stood all night in the puddled mud of the old pen and fresh green kale and turnips lay temptingly before them.

Edgar heaved himself over a net and made towards

the row of hurdles to let them on. I leant on the door, the fire crackling and spluttering behind me as the wood took hold. I saw him lean his crook against the fence, and bend forward as he loosened the shackle. One hurdle was dragged slowly back. Edgar reached the gap to lift the second hurdle clear but the toe was stuck deep in the sucking mud. Even as I watched the flock surged forward and Edgar was not quick enough. He went down like a ninepin and a grey sea of sheep, their fleeces heavy with rain, flowed over him into the green fold.

Then I was running across the field, tripping over my flapping oilskin, stumbling in my fear and anxiety to get to the old man.

He was still flat, spreadeagled, face upward in the entrance to the fold when I reached him, muddied from head to foot, hands and face, dirty, gashed and bleeding. I helped him to his feet and we both stood shaking against the hurdles. I did not try to get him to speak, just tried to wipe the mud from his face which was white as paper under the dirt. Edgar turned, still trembling, fighting for his breath, and looked at the ewes — now grazing unconcerned.

'Reckon every one ran over me. . . Reckon I'se finished, Davey. . . But I luv 'em.'

EPILOGUE

Somewhere beyond the sycamores a song-thrush sang. Blue-black rooks squabbled sleepily about their nests, now almost hidden by half-open parasols of palest green, which daily opened wider to the sun, and scattered Winter cases light to lie in drifts of pink along the lane. 'Judy, Judy... did he do it? Did he do it?'

Westward the sky took colour from the daffodils which thronged the Rectory Wood.

Up in the fold a ewe called again.

'Love. Love. Did he do it? Did he do it?' called the thrush, but no bird answered his pleading.

The first star burned, now glow-worm soft, now bright. The countryside drew down beneath the coverlet of night and below the churchyard the song of the river rose in its chanting and ran on down the valley, cool, continuous and content.